Congratulations
on your choice
to transform your life
into the full expression
of your heart's desires.

Dr Nick Hall

LET'S END ILLNESS
NOW!

with
THE BODY CHEMISTRY SUPPORT SYSTEM

Dr. Mick Hall

Conscious Publications

www.drmickhall.com/newbook

LET'S END ILLNESS NOW!

Copyright © 2006, Mick A. Hall

Let's End Illness Now!
With The Body Chemistry Support System.

First Published in December 2006

Conscious Publications
3190-A Airport Loop Dr.
Costa Mesa, Ca. 92626
Phone (714) 689-3851   fax (714) 689-3852
www.drmickhall.com

ISBN-10
0-9791478-0-8

ISBN-13
978-0-9791478-0-7

Printed in the United States of America

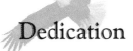

Dedication

I would like to dedicate this book to my writing buddy and mom: **Jean Ladonna Hedges Hall.**

Mom has always been my glowing example of the values of reading and organizing.

In her eighty-second year, mom has accepted the fact that age is no excuse for the way a person feels. Mom is using The Body Chemistry Support System and working out in the gym three days a week to rejuvenate her body and life.

I am very proud of the fact that she has recently come out of retirement and is launching her new writing career by writing her first in a series of children's books. She is featuring a unique character called Finny-eye-pal: a very wise and loving friend to children. Finny helps children understand the big person's world from a simplified little person's viewpoint.

Acknowledgments

I would like to express my appreciation for **Mark Victor Hansen**; for his universal desire to motivate, love and to serve everyone his life touches. I feel elated and at the same time very blessed for the honor of Mark's mentoring in my life. I would also like to acknowledge Mark for supplying me with the core title for this book.

Appreciation for my editor, Midge James:

I am beyond grateful to have the most ideal book editor for the work that I'm doing. Midge James let me know two years before I even wrote the book that she wanted to edit it. You could say that her heart was in this book long before it ever existed.

I really appreciate the crisp professionalism of Midge's work and how her expertise never changes the meaning of what I want to present; it only makes it clearer.

When she was about halfway finished editing the book, Midge shared the following kind words with me through an email:

"I just want you to know that this is going to be an extraordinary book. Your vast knowledge and experience comes popping out on every page. I feel personally overwhelmed and inspired all at the same time. Working on a project that potentially has so much meaning for the world is truly uplifting for me and I thank you again for the opportunity."

Without a doubt, I have the most wonderful and supportive office staff in the world. Thank you: Mary Hall, Janice Gaski, Rebecca Clarkson, Dean Hall, Magaly Bolvito, and Kimberly Agular for your heartfelt professionalism.

I would like to thank Mary Hall and Laura Walthers for making the cover of this book so beautiful.

Thank you Linda Kamka for your gifts, talents, and kind support. I appreciate so much Linda's gifted work of paginating and arranging the contents of the book so beautifully.

I also wish to express my appreciation to those who proofread the manuscript and offered such helpful suggestions: thank you Mary Hall, Lynn L'Ecluse, James Hopson, Candace Nugent, Jean Hall, Bonnie Bell, Dean Hall, Olgie Szaz, Jill Lloyd, and Kathy Saggiani.

I would like to acknowledge Dr. Joe Dispenza for his teachings, which allowed me to present the concept of the "automatic emotion duplicating machine" in Chapter 4.

Table Of Contents

Table Of Contents

The Journey Back Into Life

Man has wandered for so long, completely unaware of being
lost in this struggle for survival he calls "life." Yet an
awakening has begun. Like the awakening of the animals in
a great forest at dawn's first light, man is awakening to a
most profound spiritual guidance—his own intuition.

Man has experienced this guidance as absolutely accurate.
However, old habits of survival die slowly. Man's ego has been
his greatest ally in the quest for survival; yet it has also been
overwhelmingly resistant to wisdom's guiding hand.
Nevertheless, like trees in the forest pushing upward to receive
sunlight, so this great awareness continues to emerge,
creating the unfolding of a wondrous awakening...

Within this awakening is also found the inspiration for
improving our ability to hear this personal guidance.

As a result of our renewed ability to hear, important
questions arise and push themselves to the forefront of our
awareness, such as, "What is it that prematurely extinguishes
the fire of youth that is meant to passionately burn within
us to the end of our long lives?" And, "what is it that so
powerfully re-creates for us the circumstances of life that
robs us of our heart's desires?"

The voice of life speaks so clearly within each of us,
always guiding us toward life's highest expressions; and yet,
our lowered expectations automatically encourage us to push
away the abundance of life. Every day, life provides us with
new circumstances interwoven with our same old unconquered
fears. Unfortunately, these unconquered fears cause us to
hold onto our reduced expectations of life.

Who would ever have guessed that this is the cause for
every form of degenerative disease?

The human body is a brilliant communication mechanism,
always expressing how and where we hold the fears
and traumas of not only our lives, but those of our
parents as well. These deeply held fears and traumas
are expressed first as physical pain and symptoms.
If suppressed long enough, degenerative disease
is the more serious result.

Intuition is always communicating wisdom very clearly.
It is for each of us to decide when we will finally
stop and listen.

The journey back into life must begin with the awareness of
how far we have actually wandered from the heart of life,
and that focusing on those things that seem to be so
threatening to our very survival has gradually led us
deep into the valley of self-destruction.

With the awakening of this awareness comes the necessity of
making a decision, a commitment that will inspire us to
accomplish all that is required to fully restore life
back into the body.

The degree of the reader's dedication and commitment
will set the pace for this Life-restoration.
I invite you to accept this book as your road map for
The Journey Back Into Life.

Dr. Mick Hall

Introduction

One of the most intrinsic human traits is our tendency to do everything possible to avoid pain, illness or any other discomfort. When given a conscious choice, we are quite predictable in choosing comfort over pain. Yet, our common experience in life is often one of overwhelming stress and at least several physical or emotional symptoms.

In this book, I will present simple and straightforward explanations of why we experience exactly what we do, despite our desires to the contrary. The reader will be elated to find that the solutions I offer are true and life-transforming.

This book also represents a very distinct line drawn in the sand. On one side will be those who have come to learn, as I have, that it is unnecessary for anyone to suffer from illness. Standing alongside us will be wise health care professionals whose hearts are dedicated to the elimination of all levels of cause responsible for every type of illness. On the other side will be those who stand in disbelief, because they are unwilling to reconsider their long-held views on these issues. This position prevents them from reviewing and applying the principles that determine true health. Standing with them will be health care professionals and pharmaceutical companies who are concerned that, if illness is eliminated, they will no longer have a viable income or purpose. From this perspective, symptoms will continue to be treated, while all levels of cause will remain uncorrected within the body, thereby sustaining the illness industry and its financial security.

"There is a principle which is a bar against all information, which cannot fail to keep a man in everlasting ignorance—that principle is contempt prior to investigation." (Herbert Spencer, British philosopher)

Over the past 30 years, I have conducted a variety of studies and performed the necessary research to develop a system that acknowledges and supports the innate wisdom of the body. When the innate wisdom of the body is fully supported, it becomes capable of brilliantly restoring the natural functions that bring about true health.

In 1986, after years of naturopathic studies, I co-directed a holistic cancer clinic for two years. During this time, I began to discover the true questions regarding the levels of cause that needed to be answered. This experience was the launch pad for my private twenty-year research project that brought a thorough understanding of all the reasons the human body breaks down in all forms of disease.

The information I gathered and the discoveries I made from my research were invaluable tools that allowed me to understand the true needs of the body. These insights led me to develop a comprehensive support system that allows the body to restore body chemistry balance, gland and organ function and, thereby, establish a condition of true health. I refer to this system as **The Body Chemistry Support System.**

Thousands of individuals have discovered, through their personal experiences, that when the body is fully supported and provided with all its chemistry needs, true health is predictably achieved.

The body's brilliant cellular programming is what makes **The Body Chemistry Support System** work so well. When every body chemistry need is provided, the body's innate intelligence then becomes capable of handling for itself all the details for restoring natural body functions.

My intent is to focus attention upon the principles that determine true health. This book is not meant to diagnose, treat or prevent disease—that would be in direct opposition to my intent. Instead, I would like to direct the reader's focus onto this truth: "A person always travels in the direction he is looking." Let us turn our attention, together, in the direction of that which we would specifically like to create—true, vibrant, lasting health.

My most fervent hope is that this book will find its way into the hands of those who will appreciate the life-transforming truths it contains and have the courage and dedication to apply these principles to enhance their lives.

Dr. Mick Hall

CHAPTER 1

Birth of a New Life Passion

It's actually quite fascinating, when you think about it, that the further a person moves from his childhood, the keener his appreciation of some of those childhood experiences becomes. That has certainly been my experience.

As I allow myself the luxury of reminiscing about some of the special times from my youth, my sense of appreciation takes me into a place of great peace and joy. You will understand why, when I tell you that I grew up in a log cabin in the exquisite beauty of the mountains, lakes and forests of Coeur d'Alene, Idaho.

My childhood wasn't much different than it would have been had I lived a hundred years earlier. I grew up like everything in the forest: strong and healthy. The family garden, the forest and the streams supplied a great deal of our groceries, just as they would have a hundred years before. My father always provided my brothers and me with plenty of hard work. It was our own personal health club, you might say. My strong and healthy body was created by that hard work; however, it was a gift I never wanted to attribute to working hard. Isn't it interesting how difficult it can be for a young person to appreciate the life-long benefits of hard work?

Although I came into adulthood strong and healthy, my younger years taught me very little of the principles of health.

My first serious awakening came several months into my wife's first pregnancy, when I heard a report on the radio that government standards were allowing a well-known baby food company to have a certain amount of rat and mouse droppings in their baby food. I was absolutely disgusted. There was no possible way that I was ever going to allow my baby to eat food with rat droppings in it. Yet, as a first-time father, I didn't know what else I could feed my baby. This problem of 30 years ago, and my search for a solution, marked the beginning of a life-long passion to discover and understand ways to improve the quality of life. It changed my life forever in ways I could never have imagined back then.

I immediately began studying about herbs and natural therapies. I moved to Southern Idaho and studied with a naturopath who was helping people in ways that seemed almost magical. Of course, in the mid-seventies, it wasn't very common for a person to accurately utilize Iridology to discover the reasons for a person's ill health. I was fascinated to observe this naturopath identifying blockages and weaknesses in his patients' bodies, utilizing no other tool than studying their eyes. It was amazing!

During this time, my sister had been dealing with a health problem that no specialist in the northwestern states had been able to diagnose. Her physical condition and her emotional state were gradually declining. Almost every other day her heart would race to approximately 200 beats per minute and stop pumping blood. Without someone there at all times to resuscitate her, she would have died.

Fearing for her life, I explained to my sister what I believed this naturopath could do for her. I was a little disappointed that she wasn't as confident as I was with the solution I was presenting. She declined my offer, then continued by telling me not to worry, that she was leaving for the Mayo Clinic in a few days, and that they would take good care of her.

Less than three weeks later, my sister phoned with a much different attitude. She explained to me that absolutely nothing had been accomplished by her going to the Mayo Clinic and that she would like to come down to see my naturopathic doctor.

I was nervous but hopeful as, within a matter of minutes, the naturopath identified the problem areas and outlined a program that would bring about the necessary corrections. Over the next few weeks, by following the program he had outlined for her, the difficulties with which she had suffered for so long were permanently reversed. We were thrilled!

When I realized that the naturopath was able to accomplish what none of the other doctors could, this realization inspired me with the desire to dedicate my life to understanding the human body and the principles that determine its true well-being.

A View From The Other Side Of The World

It was in early December of 1977 that my homesick South African wife, our two young sons and I packed our things and moved to South Africa. No matter what the future held for us, or what would transpire in South Africa, I knew that my highest priority would be to continue my studies. On our way, we stopped in England for a few days so I could meet with a college professor who had written several books on healing modalities in which I was particularly interested. While we were at his college, I purchased a naturopathic home study course that he had developed.

For the next three years, I worked hard and studied harder. About six months after arriving in South Africa, Dr. Martin Pretorius came to my office, where I was doing nutritional counseling and bodywork. Shortly thereafter, we combined our efforts by expanding my office to include our newly formed Health Education Center. This was a great and unexpected opportunity for me, particularly since the curriculum included a library of videotapes that Dr. Pretorius had made from classes he had been teaching. I took advantage of such a priceless library of videos by viewing every one of them dozens of times in the evenings.

When Dr. Pretorius and I started working together in 1978, he was a 74-year-old walking health encyclopedia. Dating back to the 1930s, he was one of the original pioneers of the health movement. His work helped bring about advances in natural healing, and many of the natural options we now enjoy in the

United States can be credited to his efforts. I will always be grateful for the valuable insights I garnered from being mentored by Dr. Pretorius.

One of the highlights of my work in South Africa was a seven-year-old girl, who, when I met her, had just returned home from having a malignant brain tumor removed. The little girl's mother was referred to me by a couple I knew who were passionate and convincing about their belief in my ability to help her. As a result, the mother offered her complete trust, and committed herself to following to the letter the instructions I developed for her daughter. A year later, I received a letter from the girl's mother thanking me for my coaching and help. She said she would never want any of her other children to have to experience what her youngest went through with her cancer, but she sure wished her other children were as healthy as the youngest turned out to be after following the program I had outlined for her.

By the time I had been in South Africa for three years, I had made many new friends who had allowed me to assist them in reversing their health challenges. It was a very special feeling to have so many people expressing such appreciation for the help I had provided them.

Then, one evening in August of 1980, my whole world came crashing down. As I pulled into the driveway after work, my wife met me at my car. Something was very different. There were no smiles or happy greetings, just a deeply worried look on her face and an open letter in her hand. Without a greeting, her voice breaking, she said, "you have to go to America right away." I could tell that, if she spoke another word, the restrained flood of tears would be unleashed, so I took the letter and read it for myself. Written nearly a week before by my sister from Idaho, the letter briefly reviewed the gradual decline of our youngest brother's health over the previous couple of months, and ended with, "he just came out of a coma and isn't expected to live much longer."

It is devastating to lose any family member. Jeff was eleven years younger than I and had always seemed more like a son to me than a brother. To think of him dying at seventeen years of age was unbearable.

By 10:00 the next morning, I was flying to Houston, Texas. It seemed that a funeral was inevitable, but my wife and I felt that if I got there immediately, maybe by some miracle I could do something to help him.

My parents drove me directly to the hospital from the airport. I knew that Jeff was doing poorly, but I didn't expect to see him looking as though he was dying of starvation. He was just skin and bones and in an almost total vegetative state. His eyes refused to track anything that moved. Although he was looking right at me as I spoke to him, it broke my heart to see that he was totally unaware that I, or anyone else, was in the room.

My parents filled me in on how he was injured while boxing in a U.S. National Finalist bout—one of the last matches to determine who would represent the U.S. in the next Olympics—and how he went into convulsions as our brother Scott was driving him to the hospital, and how the surgeon had to drill a hole into his skull to relieve the pressure from trapped spinal fluids unable to flow down his spinal cord. They also described how, during his operation, he had died for such a long time before they could resuscitate him that his doctor believed he would never recover from the damage.

Just then, Jeff's neurosurgeon entered the room. He was a very compassionate and caring man. I could tell that it was very difficult for him to tell us what he had to say. He explained that Jeff's veins had collapsed and that the nurse had just removed his last IV. They were expecting him to die within the next 48 hours.

By this time I was in a mild state of shock and feeling like I was caught somewhere between a very bad dream and a life experience in which I didn't want to be involved.

Through my numbed perception, I was vaguely aware of my

mother, Jean, telling the surgeon that I was a naturopath and asking if he would allow me to work with Jeff nutritionally. My state of shock was such that I barely realized that he had actually agreed. However, he also gave me a dozen reasons why I shouldn't be too hopeful about being able to help Jeff. He told me again of Jeff's death experience, his total paralysis, the brain damage caused by his death experience (and substantiated by x-rays), his kidney and other infections and, of course, the collapsing of his veins, indicating the body was shutting down and preparing to die. Completing this bleak picture was the obvious fact that he had deteriorated from a vital, muscular athlete to nothing but skin and bones.

Jeff's neurosurgeon was very emphatic as he explained: "I don't believe it is possible for you to stabilize Jeff's life but, if you were able to do this, the best you could hope for is that he would live in a vegetative state." He looked over at the nurse who was doing her best to feed Jeff some melted vanilla ice cream, then continued by sharing some of his best nutritional advice, which included the virtues of melted vanilla ice cream.

As the doctor left the room, I turned to the nurse and asked her to please find someone who could carefully install a gastrointestinal tube into Jeff's stomach so we could feed him more easily.

Not knowing how long this small window of opportunity would remain open, I asked my parents to drive me around to gather some supplies with which to work. After finding all the necessary ingredients, we returned to the large boat on which my parents and brothers had been living. There I blended some raw liver in water, with crushed papain tablets, alfalfa sprouts, and other whole food items. After pressing the mixture through a sieve to separate the liquid from the solid material, we rushed back to the hospital with a jar of the most horrible looking greenish-brown liquid you could imagine.

The inspiration for this liquid came from my work in South Africa as well as from an old mink rancher I had known as a teen. I remembered watching the old rancher take a mink from its cage that looked as though it were already dead. He cut a small strip of fresh beef liver and, with a small round piece of wood, pushed the liver down the mink's throat into its stomach. He returned the mink to its cage. Within an hour, I was amazed to see the same mink running around as though it had never been ill.

Two days of injecting this liquid into Jeff's stomach through the G.I. tube gave proof that we had indeed stabilized his life. We had taken the very first step on a journey for which we had no road map.

It was sad that only my family and I had shifted our expectations regarding the outcome of the doctor's prognosis. After the first 48 hours had passed, all the nurses who knew of Jeff's case commented on how amazing it was that he was still alive. At first, I thought the nurses were as excited as we were about the hope that, once we stabilized Jeff's life, we might be able to take him to the next step. It was only much later that I realized the nurses believed as the doctor did, that we were just resisting the inevitable, forcing this poor vegetative boy to remain alive when we should be allowing him to pass on.

After a week we were being called to the hospital every night at about midnight with this news: "We think Jeff is passing away now." We would rush over as quickly as possible and, upon our arrival, find him mildly convulsing. One such time we found him so uncomfortable with thirst that he was convulsing from dehydration. The other two times he had fallen slightly to one side and was lying on his arm, causing such pain and discomfort that he was shaking all over. Each time, after we relieved the reasons for his discomfort, he would be fine again.

The fourth late night visit proved to us that Jeff's only chance for survival would be for us to get him away from the hospital and completely take over his care.

When we arrived that night, Jeff was stripped to his underpants and lying on a mat of tubes with ice cold water running through them, and there were two huge fans blowing on his body at high speed. Jeff was in a strong and constant convulsion, with goose bumps all over his body.

Despite all the activity of the previous five minutes, the nurse was still standing there holding the thermometer. When we entered the room, she was shaking her head and saying, "I didn't know anybody could live with a temperature of 108 degrees."

It wasn't until the next afternoon that Jeff was finally comfortable enough to stop shaking and convulsing. As we assessed his condition, for the first time since I arrived from South Africa I finally stopped to really think about what an impossible challenge we had undertaken. Besides all the problems of the week before, it was now evident that we were dealing with a whole new level of difficulties. The fever and convulsions had left his calf muscles contracted so tightly we were unable to get his feet into a normal position. This forced his toes to permanently point straight down. And, although there was a dead stare to his eyes before, they were now permanently misaligned, both eyes drifting toward the outside corners of the sockets. Besides these two obvious problems, there was no doubt that such a high fever had probably destroyed more of his brain.

Reflecting on all these obstacles, I allowed myself for the first time to silently admit that what we had been attempting was impossible. Maybe the doctor was correct in his assessment of how impossible it would be for all that Jeff had lost to be restored, and that we were allowing our fears of Jeff's death to make us do foolish things.

When I recovered from that line of thought, I shifted back into "auto pilot" and began looking for a home we could move Jeff into. I suppose Jeff's doctor would have considered me one of those individuals incapable of coming to his senses.

After a few days, I found a large home that had been used for years as a clinic. For the past dozen years, it had been empty and abandoned. I found the owner and offered to make the house livable in exchange for a low rent. The owner had been holding onto the property for the land value and just hadn't got around to tearing down the house. Because I was very persistent and the owner had nothing to lose, he finally agreed.

Since the house had been empty for so long, it had 56 broken window panes, loads of trash from homeless people and kids, no water, no electricity and as much dirt inside as there was in the back yard. Still, in less than two weeks—with the help of family and friends—the house was cleaned up, furnished and made quite livable. We set up one of the bedrooms with an adjustable hospital bed for Jeff and, with that, we were ready to bring him home.

At first Mom and I were a bit intimidated by the doctor and nurses advising us that, if we were to take Jeff from the hospital, we would be completely responsible for whatever happened to him. We stopped and thought for a second about what they were saying, then got very excited as we realized that whatever would happen to him at home would be so much better than what had been happening to him in the hospital. Mom very courageously signed the release papers, we put Jeff into the makeshift bed we created for him in the back of an old station wagon, and took him to his new home.

I was unable to massage Jeff in the beginning because of the hundreds of small lumps all over his body caused by malnutrition from his hospital stay. So, we set up a schedule of range-of-motion exercises for him, continued his nutrient solution and began a program for intestinal evacuation.

Since Jeff's whole problem began with the misalignment of the upper vertebrae of his neck, we were grateful when Dr. Greg White, a chiropractor and friend of the family, kindly offered to come to the house and administer chiropractic treatments.

Jeff had been home for a few weeks by this time, receiving the powerful nutrition and the other supportive treatments every day. Within 24 hours of his first chiropractic treatment Jeff was able to manage a very slight wiggle in one hand. By the second treatment, it became obvious that his paralysis was beginning to be reversed. Jeff had also begun to indicate with his eyes that he was aware of what we were doing. This was extremely exciting, because it proved he wasn't just in a vegetative state. Without a doubt this was a major turning point and, for the first time, we were able to have some real hope.

Over the next couple of months, Jeff's progress was slow, but steady. He was able to do simple exercises and was getting stronger by the day. The only problem was that, after the first little wiggle of his hand, it seemed to take forever for him to get strong enough to just sit up in a wheelchair and his communication skills were still limited to blinking his eyes.

Out of necessity, our brother Scott and I had to shift our focus into generating an income. We directed most of our time and attention to the Texas oil fields, which left our mom to be the chief 24-hour-a-day caregiver and life support system for Jeff.

My wife and children left South Africa and joined me in October. By the end of November, I had been in Texas for three very long months. Thanksgiving came and we were a big happy family, so proud of Jeff's exciting progress. By this time, he just seemed to be getting stronger and healthier every day.

With all his progress, it still took Scott and me a while to get Jeff propped up and stabilized well enough in his wheelchair to be able to join us at the Thanksgiving table. Since all his nutrition still had to be put through his feeding tube, Mom decided that (for psychological purposes) she would blend up a little of the mashed potatoes, gravy and turkey and put that down the tube. As far as we could tell, he was pleased with his dinner and I know he enjoyed being able to sit around the table with the family again.

By the time Christmas dinner came around Jeff had become much more animated. This time he could actually eat little bits of food. When dinner was nearly over it seemed as though Jeff was getting very impatient. He was holding his hands in front of his body with his index fingers together and his thumbs touching.

A guessing game continued until Mom said the word "pie." By this time, Jeff was communicating by blinking once for no and twice for yes. When he heard the word pie he almost started a windstorm with his eyelashes. We soon realized that Thanksgiving dinner had activated such a strong craving for pumpkin pie that Jeff was absolutely tormented for the entire time between the two holidays.

Once he got a taste of pumpkin pie, he couldn't stop eating it. We were just so thrilled to see him happy that we pulled his feeding tube out and let him eat all the pie he wanted. He ate at least half a pie by himself that evening. He had been hurting and sacrificing for so long, to watch him eating that pumpkin pie was like watching an exuberant child at a birthday party.

By noon the next day word had spread that Jeff was eating pie. Within hours the kitchen was filled with pies brought by Jeff's friends, his girlfriend, family friends, and relatives. We couldn't stop him. He had become a pie-eating machine. All day long, for days on end, Jeff sat with his visitors—who were so excited about how well he was doing—and ate pie. By the end of the fourth day he finally stopped eating pie and wasn't able to hold his head up very well. Mom asked him if he wanted the tube put back in. He sadly blinked his eyes to say yes. As much fun as eating the pies had been, Jeff could feel his energy draining away. From his experience with the pies, Jeff recognized without a doubt the healing power of the nutrient mixture we had been giving him.

By the time we reached the one-year mark, Jeff had learned to walk and talk again. He was still quite weak, but close to being able to take care of himself. By this time he could feed himself, but now his body was so accustomed to having only pure nutrients that any sort of junk food was repulsive to him.

Jeff continued with a very healthy nutrition plan. I wasn't too surprised, though, that he dropped the raw liver from his diet the second his feeding tube was removed. Although the tube protected him from having to taste the liver, he did let me know that, as far as he was concerned, there wasn't anything worse than a raw liver burp.

For the first couple of months after Jeff learned to walk he had to jog on his tiptoes to stretch his calf muscles and tendons. After returning to Coeur d'Alene, he went to the gym and began working out as often as possible to build up his body again. He finished high school, had two surgeries to realign his eyes, volunteered to fulfill a year-and-a-half-long mission for his church, and soon after married his sweetheart Wanda, whom he had met shortly after returning to Coeur d'Alene.

At the time of this writing, it has been twenty-six years since my return to America to help Jeff. Jeff invested about six years of extremely hard work to shift himself from being a human vegetable into a man living a completely normal life. His diligence in the fulfillment of his church responsibilities has been on par with his diligence in his work and his dedication as a husband and father. Anyone who did not know his history would find it almost impossible to believe that he was ever disabled in any way.

Personally, I couldn't be happier with the outcome of my return to the United States. My mind could be filled right now with the horrible memories of my little brother dying and my having to attend his funeral. Instead, a few days ago Jeff and I, along with Jeff's 14-year-old son Matthew, were in their back yard playing like kids, hitting balls back and forth to each other. I much prefer the memories we continue to make over those that could have been.

Working with Jeff provided a dramatic affirmation for me that I was on the "right track." It made me even more determined to understand how the body really functions and how to reverse the health challenges that seemed completely out of control.

In 1986, I was introduced to the American Metabolic Institute, one of the cancer clinics in Mexico. After discovering the valuable services available through this facility, I started driving a friend to the clinic for weekly therapy. He had suffered a stroke several months before and had hired me to provide him with special in-home therapy.

At the clinic, I became familiar with the staff and clinic operations, since there wasn't much else for me to do while my friend was receiving his colonics and other treatments. By our fourth or fifth visit, I was feeling very much a part of the clinic and the work they were involved in, so it wasn't much of a shock when I was invited to join the staff as co-director of the clinic.

My time at the clinic provided me with deep insights regarding the extreme suffering that disease can inflict upon the human body. I was also encouraged by the awareness that better solutions were available than most people were being informed of.

After two years, I hit a saturation point of disappointment. As much hope as our success was providing for our patients, I was surprised and upset at how often I would catch myself working harder to save a person's life than they were willing to work for themselves. I felt strongly moved to find a deeper understanding of how this could be so.

I became determined to fully understand two essential issues: all levels of cause responsible for the development of degenerative disease, and the self-destructive role of the individual in this process.

I realized that, in order to conduct a broad enough search to find the answers I was looking for, I would need to leave the clinic. I had a clear idea of the questions I wanted answered regarding the chemistry of the human body, as well as the levels of cause responsible for the development of degeneration. I felt driven to understand why some people, like Jeff, would commit their hearts and souls to getting well, while others waited for someone to "fix" them, or for the body to just miraculously heal itself.

Over the past 20 years, I have performed over 20,000 individual health screens, all of which included from one to two hours of personal consulting. Each health screen included the Darkfield as well as the HLB blood studies. These are two techniques of viewing an individual's blood to assess blockages within vital pathways of the body and to determine the body's strengths, weaknesses and the reasons behind its problems. Simply stated, in place of a diagnosis, my screening was a way for me to understand the levels of cause for the body to break down in all forms of degenerative disease.

During the first few years of my research, I included a twelve-step chemistry evaluation of the urine, and often evaluated and interpreted the results of tissue mineral analyses. All this gave me a very clear overview of the complete fluid chemistry of the human body.

During this 20-year period, I earned my doctorate in naturopathy and gained an invaluable understanding of all levels of cause involved in the aging and degeneration of the human body. I developed and evolved a comprehensive educational health program and personally formulated a complete system of nutritional products for supporting the innate wisdom of the body to re-establish the balance of true health.

The remainder of this book is a simplified presentation that will allow you to clearly understand exactly how and why the human body ages and breaks down in every form of degeneration.

By the time you finish reading this book you will come to understand that there is no reason for a person to suffer with any form of degenerative disease, and that the pain and discomforts that generally accompany the aging process are also unnecessary.

There is no reason for
a person to suffer with any
form of degenerative disease,
and the pain and discomforts
that generally accompany
the aging process are
also unnecessary.

CHAPTER 2

Life Always Gives You Exactly What You Expect, No More, And No Less

A principle is defined as one of the basic underlying laws that determine how life works. It doesn't matter whether we believe in a principle or not, it is always the same. It is forever true and will never be different. Principles are the eternal structural standards that maintain universal order.

The principle I would like to share with you is one which you are undoubtedly much more familiar with than you realize. The clarity of this information will make this principle either the scariest part of your life, or one of the most exciting, depending on what you do with the information presented.

My suggestion is that you learn everything possible about this principle and how to work within its positive guidelines. This principle determines the outcome of every circumstance of your life!

Life always gives you exactly what you expect, no more, and no less.

Let's call this **The Principle of Expectation.** Through this principle, our own expectations cause us to set the guidelines and parameters for every circumstance in our lives. Most people know this principle to be true. We have all watched ourselves pushing away that which we have perceived to be beyond our comfort zone. It is crucial to develop a deep understanding of the fact that this comfort level is dictated by our expectations of life.

I would say that it is in every human being's very best interest to fully understand the origin of this principle's near-dictatorial power over our lives.

The big-time lottery winners, back when the winnings were awarded in one lump sum, are perfect examples of how universally established this principle is. To receive such a large sum of money was an absolute dream come true for the lucky winners. Nevertheless, it was observed that, in most cases, their lives were turned upside down and most of the money was dissipated within a surprisingly short time.

Such a large sum of money, received so quickly and unexpectedly, was far beyond the expectations of these lucky winners. As crazy as it seems, such a large amount of money forced them out of the comfort zone of their expectations of life. **The Principle of Expectation** dictated that, one way or another, the money had to go, so that they could reestablish their comfort zone of expectation.

This principle is so far-reaching that it imposes its limitations onto every value within our personal lives: physically, emotionally, spiritually, monetarily and in all our relationships with others. We know it, we observe it, and we fight it every day of our lives.

Since the principle of cause and effect also regulates how our world functions, it doesn't matter how well we fight against the effects in our lives, they will continue to reappear until we correct the cause or causes.

The real purpose of this book is to bring the **Principle of Expectation** out into the light and provide you with such a complete solution that there will no longer be any reason for the desires of your heart to be withheld from you. This book exemplifies the statement, "you will know the truth, and the truth will set you free." Free from what, you might ask? For starters, from the most limiting force imprisoning our entire lives, **The Principle of Expectation,** where each of us personally maintains his or her own confinement and limitations.

Let's imagine our expectations as an opening that leads into our personal lives. It is sort of like the mail slot in the front door of a house. Maybe it would be a little easier to imagine that the opening is a few times larger than a regular mail slot. This imaginary opening now represents the portal through which we receive all that life has to offer us. The problem is, the size of this opening limits so many of our desires. However, the principle is as constant as the size of that opening. We are only able to receive that which will fit through the opening.

Obviously, the desired result is to understand the mechanics of this principle so well that we can discover how to expand this portal, thereby allowing ourselves to receive much more of the good that life has to offer.

Since the portal that limits the delivery of good into our lives is created from our own expectations, it makes sense that enlarging and expanding our expectations will automatically expand the flow of good into our lives. So, let's consider for a moment exactly what an expectation really is, and how it originated.

An expectation is defined as: *a confident belief or a strong hope that a particular event will happen; a mental image of something expected, often compared to its reality.*

So, an expectation is the same thing as a **"confident belief."** And what is a belief? A belief is defined as: *an acceptance by the mind that something is true or real; an opinion, especially a firm and considered one.* Simply stated, then: a belief is a **strongly considered opinion.** When it is all put together, we have this: **an expectation** is a **strongly considered opinion.**

This truth underscores the importance of a person choosing carefully the opinions he considers valuable enough to present to life, for the circumstances of that life will be created from those opinions.

Now, let's do a little historic review to determine where our strongly considered opinions may have originated. Our parents are usually the first source of our opinions regarding life. We are also influenced by our teachers, friends, relatives, society, television and other media, and, of course, by the opinions we form for ourselves as we experience life.

There is one more very powerful source from which our opinions are formed. As strong an influence as the opinions of our parents are, let's not forget the main source of *their* opinions. That's right, the DNA memories of our four grandparents exist in every cell of our bodies, and play a major role in the development of our opinions.

All together, our strongly considered opinions establish what we refer to as our **belief system,** which is **the cause for our expectations, and the governing influence of the circumstances of our lives.**

Let's not confuse the power of belief (or the faith that brings miracles into our lives) with our base belief systems. The former is a power for receiving all that is good, while the latter is the most limiting and destructive force in our lives.

Before we look at some of the limiting beliefs that directly inhibit the good from flowing into our lives, let's consider the following question: **If life beat you up yesterday, what will you expect from life tomorrow**? Of course, you'll naturally expect more of the same. This is exactly how the status quo of our expectations of life establishes its continuous pattern of repetition.

When we conduct an honest self-evaluation of our lives as adults, what are some of our findings? We may discover that we respond to certain circumstances in the same way we observed one of our parents responding in the past. An interesting twist on that is how we sometimes create our own response by rebelling and doing just the opposite of what one of our parents would have done. What about the opinions we so often heard one or the other parent express, and what influence has that had on the decisions we make in our own lives? By conducting such an evaluation, we can usually discover many of the limiting beliefs we have unconsciously imposed on ourselves.

Winston Churchill once stated: *"The truth is incontrovertible. Malice may attack it, ignorance may deride it, but in the end, there it is."*

An interesting fact of life is that **truth** never needs to be defended. The human ego, on the other hand, carries a strong habitual vested interest in defending its personal beliefs and opinions about what it believes to be true.

Since we are all guilty of defending our beliefs, let's look at the emotion that gets activated when we feel obligated to do so. What occurs is a shift into the emotion of fear—fear of being vulnerable, fear that we will be made wrong, again. It is the same as the need to defend ourselves under *any* circumstance.

A strong survival trait of the human ego is doing whatever it takes to be right. As a result of this ego trait, for thousands of years it was interwoven into the lives of our ancestors that everyone who had a different opinion must be wrong. Those who were considered "wrong" were seen as different and unacceptable (and often dangerous) and, therefore, it was justifiable for those who considered themselves to be right to attack or destroy those they deemed to be "wrong."

The process of survival, unfortunately, is not an expression of love and joy. It is a fear-based drive to avoid pain, suffering and physical death. Therefore, the driving force behind survival is always fear. As long as we are locked into a survival mode, we are driven by fear, which sends us back into our fear-based belief systems, and our inevitable negative **expectations of life.**

I'm not saying that our belief systems are wrong. It's just that the time has come to re-evaluate them, and eliminate those that are in opposition to our best interests. A belief system, the core of our survival mechanism, is exactly like the starter on an engine. We need it to start the engine but, when the engine starts, the starter must be disengaged because it cannot turn as fast as the engine. If it isn't disengaged soon after the engine starts, it can destroy itself and the engine with it.

Humanity has been surviving for thousands of years. The fact that we are all still alive is absolute proof that a fear-based survival system works. But the time has arrived for us to learn how to **actually live,** so that we no longer need to merely survive.

When we take a closer look at the components of a belief system, we see that each one is a fear-based opinion regarding the best ways to survive.

As adults, we have the opportunity to evaluate each of our beliefs. We can discard those that don't work for us. When we find one that *does* work for us, we can add it to our collection, making it a part of our belief system. Our individual beliefs are personal, time-tested techniques for making our lives work the best way we can. That is why we are so protective of them. We defend our belief systems with fear and caution because deep inside we believe that, if someone took away our beliefs, we would no longer be able to survive.

Such a belief is actually true, but then again, who really wants to continue just surviving? **It's time to let go of survival and embrace the extraordinary joy of really living!**

As long as we are only surviving, relief from suffering will be the greatest experience of life we can expect. Unfortunately, relief from suffering is the generally accepted experience we refer to as **enjoyment.** It is the pleasant scratch for what itches, the euphoric quenching of a strong thirst, the refreshing plunge into a pool of cool water on a hot day, the peaceful calm after the storm, the needed relaxation and entertainment in celebration of a job well done. None of these experiences has much to do with pure joy, and each gets its power from the contrasting suffering immediately preceding the celebrated relief. Every one of these examples, and most experiences in our lives that we refer to as joyful experiences, is actually nothing more than **the relief from suffering.**

Relief from suffering is an enjoyable reprieve from the harsh side of survival, while real joy is the motivating attraction of truly living, of consciously creating our hearts' desires. In other words, **the pain of survival pushes, until we allow the joy of living to pull.**

In Chapter 26, we will discuss how to shift from our habitual survival mode into life and the true process of living.

The pain of survival
pushes, until we allow
the joy of living to pull.

CHAPTER 3

Redefining The Word *Health*

There aren't many words in our modern vocabulary more distorted and abused than the word *health*. Here are a few examples of the ways people distort that word:

- Millions of people use the word *health* in reference to their own state of existence but have never experienced how it really feels to be healthy.
- We have very **fit** athletes who are suffering with the effects of poor health.
- The average person believes that, if he doesn't have a debilitating disease or a symptom that puts him in bed, he is "basically healthy."
- Consider the 60-year-old who has all levels of cause for a fatal degenerative disease well established within his body. However, because he doesn't have a diagnosable disease quite yet, and because his physician tells him he is "fine" and gives him a "clean bill of health," he foolishly agrees that he is "healthy," when he knows better.
- And how about our system of *disease monitoring and treatment* being referred to as *"health care?"*
- And what about our *"health insurance"* that has absolutely nothing to do with insuring us of health, but rather charges huge amounts of money to assist in paying for drugs, medical evaluations and surgeries?

These examples are so far removed from an honest representation of health that they only insult the word. **The health of anything has to do with its soundness, vitality and proper functioning—its overall integrity.**

When it comes to the human body, its soundness, vitality and proper functioning are the result of how freely the essence and substances of life are able to flow throughout the five vital pathways of the body.

The five vital pathways are:

- The intestinal tract;
- The bloodstream;
- The lymphatic system;
- The nervous system; and
- The meridians.

In fact, to emphasize how vital it is to keep these pathways open and flowing, the reader should consider this truth: if all five pathways were kept completely open and the essence and substances of life flowing freely, without obstruction, **it would be impossible for any form of disease to develop or remain within the body**. Just think how liberating that idea is at a time when so much helpless fear is being generated around the subject of disease. **To conceive of disease as a predictable result of causal factors that can all be avoided or reversed is truly exhilarating**. For the thousands of individuals to whom I have already taught these principles, the confident application of this concept has greatly reduced the unnecessary fear that has been attached to the subject of disease, as they have watched their own pain and symptoms disappear.

Most people in the United States are conditioned to believe what is subtly being presented as nearly inevitable: **that, at some point in time, they are going to develop a life-threatening, debilitating disease**.

The truth is, **the natural state of the human body is the balance of vital health**, and vital health is only lost when it gets destroyed through the eleven ways described in Chapters 8, 9 and 10.

The reason I believe it is essential to properly redefine the word "health" is because, without an accurate and true definition for such a key word, **true communication** on the subject of health remains confusing, vague or nonexistent.

In the previous chapter we discussed how our viewpoint from the perspective of survival leads us to believe that joy is defined as the relief from suffering. That may feel like an accurate observation from the perspective of survival, but it isn't the truth.

From the same viewpoint of survival, the word *health* could be considered to mean the absence of symptoms, pain and disease. But as incorrect as it is to define the word *joy* as relief from the intensity of suffering, **it is equally incorrect to refer to the relief an individual enjoys in the absence of symptoms and disease as the definition of health. Both definitions are relative, flexible and false.**

The true definition of any word must be established from the substance the word represents, not in contrast to what it isn't.

Defining human health has nothing to do with any contrasting condition, nothing to do with organizations and their functions, nothing to do with the viewpoints handed down by our parents. **True health has to do with the integrity of the trillions of tissue cells that make up the body. It has to do with the overall vitality, systemic harmony and proper functioning of every gland, organ and system within the body.**

One of the most popular experiments of the past hundred years was when Dr. Alexis Carrel kept the tissue cells from a chicken alive for many times the life expectancy of a chicken. He kept the cells in an ideally supportive environment, proving that **death and disease are not conditions whose cause can be found within the tissue cells. The immediate cause of death and disease is found in the fluids surrounding the cells!** In other words, Dr. Carrel proved that, if the immediate environment of the body's tissue cells were kept clean and the necessary nutrients made available, **tissue cells would continue reproducing themselves perfectly, *forever.***

Therefore, the foundation for the health of the human body must be established with a clean systemic fluid environment that protects the brilliant programming that was input into every cell by the creator of the human body. **If this could be maintained, disease would be impossible!**

A new definition for the word health could finally be introduced as: *The Unlimited Physical Expression Of Life.*

A new definition for the
word health could finally
be introduced as:
The Unlimited Physical
Expression Of Life.

CHAPTER 4

The Body Is The Crystallized Form Of Our Emotional Expressions

When I was six years old, my mother was walking by the Great Salt Lake in Utah when she saw a beautiful crystallized salt formation on the end of a bridge, close to the water. The water splashing onto the end of a bridge beam, and the wind and sun drying the layers of salt water, formed a unique mass of beautiful crystals about three inches thick and about the diameter of a large dinner plate. Whenever I think about the powerful influence our emotions have on our bodies, it reminds me of that unique mass of salt crystals and the way it was formed.

Most adults are aware of the connection between the stresses of life and the tension held in their necks, shoulders, and backs; but, beyond such an obvious example, not much thought is generally given to the relationship between our emotions and our physiology (the way our bodies work).

The truth is, thoughts select emotions, emotions regulate chemistry, and chemistry determines physiology. If every person would just carry this thought in the forefront of his mind, it would come close to eliminating the mysteries of health and disease.

Let's look at how our thoughts select our emotions.

Thoughts are like the spinning arrow on a board game; the direction it points selects the subject matter to be focused upon. As adults, we have had so many experiences during our lifetimes, every one of which is associated with either a "good" emotion or a "bad" emotion. Because of our vast experience, every thought associated with our lives is now charged with emotional energy. No matter how subtle, there will always be at least a mild stimulation of emotion attached to every subject to which we direct our thoughts. In fact, it is nearly impossible to separate the emotion from *any* thought.

If you look at a photograph of a beautiful green pasture with several lush shade trees, a crystal clear stream, and a mare with her newborn colt, you might feel how easy and natural it is to shift into a state of peace and joy.

Now, imagine yourself looking at a clear photograph of an accident scene showing a crying mother being restrained as paramedics place her deceased child into an ambulance. Do you feel how quickly your emotions shift into pain and sorrow?

About 35 years ago, I read a statement that made such a strong impression upon me that I couldn't get it out of my mind. The statement was from the book, *Psycho Cybernetics,* by Maxwell Multz. In his book, Dr. Multz stated, "the human brain and nervous system are incapable of determining the difference between an actual experience and one imagined in detail." Dr. Multz went on to describe the many experiments he personally performed to prove how factual this principle is.

That is such a powerful insight into why it is so stressful for a person to keep reviewing the details of any tragic experience, or to repeatedly watch the details of a natural disaster as it gets televised. The entire nervous system believes that the same horrible occurrence is happening all over again each time it is viewed, because the brain and nervous system cannot tell the difference between the actual tragedy and the detailed reviews.

Just think how many tons of anti-depressants are sold every time there is a national tragedy and the news channels review the details every few minutes for days at a time. Unfortunately, there are millions of people who unwittingly watch the hundreds of detailed reviews, and, in the process, destroy their own hope and well-being and thereby become depressed.

Scientists in the field of quantum physics (the study of the energetic composition of life and matter) are now providing even more clarity about what takes place within the brain and nervous system when attention is focused in a direction that activates feelings of any form of emotional distress or discomfort.

When we focus our thoughts on a subject that evokes any negative emotion—such as fear, anger, sadness or despair—a chemical reaction takes place inside our bodies, immediately and automatically.

To complicate matters even more, the brain can't even tell the difference between an actual experience and a **memory**! This is why the chemical reactions explode within our bodies every time we are reminded of a traumatic experience.

The hypothalamus is found in a central area on the under-side of the human brain. The hypothalamus is like a mini-factory that assembles specific chemicals that match specific emotions that we experience. These specific chemicals, referred to as neuro-peptides or neuro-hormones, are small-chained amino acid sequences. The hypothalamus is able to produce a vast volume of neuro-hormones, almost instantly, to match any emotional state we experience in our daily lives. There is a specific neuro-hormone produced for anger, another for sadness, and another for fear and so on.

The moment we focus upon a thought associated with any former emotional state, the hypothalamus instantly begins producing the exact neuro-hormone to match the remembered emotional state, and releases it into the bloodstream through the pituitary gland. The instant the neuro-hormones are released into the bloodstream, they rapidly find their way to specific centers within the body.

The surface of every cell in the human body has hundreds and sometimes thousands of receptor sites. When the neuro-hormones dock themselves into the receptor sites, they act like a key in a lock that actually shifts the receptor site, sending a message into the cell. All similar neuro-hormones send the same message into the cells. If the hypothalamus sends out neuro-hormones that match the emotional state of a memory involving anger, every neuro-hormone sends that message into every cell to instantly recreate a whole body experience of anger.

The same experience is repeated for every emotional state in our memories.

Each one of us faces a serious problem when it comes to this automatic emotion-duplicating machine. That is, our emotional habits are actually **addictions**. A drug like heroin uses the very same cellular receptor sites and, by doing so, determines an individual's emotional state.

Habitual, or addictive, emotional states drive every one of us to do the things we do in excess, or in a way that becomes self-destructive. Whenever we repeat any action that doesn't enhance our lives, we can be assured that our little neuro-hormone, **emotion-duplicating machine** has been activated. Unfortunately, if we were to monitor our lives closely, we would discover that this automatic duplicating machine is firing dozens of times every day and is responsible for propelling our lives in the direction that still doesn't work for us—the direction of our self-destruction.

So, what does all of this have to do with the health of our bodies? This is exactly how our memories of traumatic experiences **crystallize in our physical bodies, converting these experiences into symptoms and disease**.

Our thoughts select our
emotions, our emotions
regulate our chemistry,
and our chemistry
determines our physiology.

CHAPTER 5
Vitality of Youth Restored

I will always be grateful that I had the opportunity and the ability to help Jeff (my youngest brother) live beyond the 48 hours he was given, and to watch him as he became one of the healthiest young men of his age group.

When I began working with Jeff, I would have given anything for access to the information contained within this book. Now that this information is available, the only thing left for anyone to do is to generate the necessary motivation to transfer the information from the book into his or her own life.

To help with this motivation, I would like to share a few short stories about some of the people I have worked with who became sufficiently motivated to do the work necessary to earn their well-deserved rewards.

I'd like to begin with a visit I had last year with my oldest brother Darwin. We were in Coeur d'Alene at the time. During our conversation, Dar informed me that the following week when he returned home to San Antonio, he was scheduled to have his prostate surgically removed. He had been aware for some time that problems were brewing in that area of his body, but recently his medical doctor had informed him of the increased size of a cancerous tumor protruding from the prostate.

For an hour or two, I shared with him observations I had made over the past few years of men with prostate problems who had applied the simple principles I was sharing with him.

Since Dar and his wife are both registered nurses, I thought he was just being polite by remaining in the conversation with me for so long. I was very pleasantly surprised at the end of our conversation when he smiled and said, "well, let's do it!"

The following week I outlined a very strict program that he began following to the letter. As time passed, I was shocked to find that Dar was following his program more strictly than most people I had ever worked with. Being aware of how closely he was adhering to his program, I wasn't surprised at all when, four months later, he told me that his tumor was gone and he was completely healthy.

A few weeks after he shared his great news, he and his wife went on a Caribbean cruise. He phoned me a few days after they returned from the cruise. They enjoyed themselves so much, Dar just couldn't stop talking about the cruise. He also admitted to being very pleased at being able to take his healthy prostate on the cruise with them.

The urologist who confirmed the health of Dar's prostate is Dr. Ian Thompson. Dr. Thompson co-authored the book, *Prostate Cancer*. During Dar's first visit with Dr. Thompson, he said, "you probably don't know this, but I'm the world's expert on prostate cancer."

Dr. Thompson asked quite a few questions and puzzled over the biopsy report that so recently showed positive for a Gleason Six prostate cancer. He ended by saying, "I don't know what you've been doing but whatever it is, keep it up." Dar has seen Dr. Thompson every four months since then and, every time, the doctor says the same thing: "Whatever you're doing, keep it up."

It has been about 18 months since Dar began his program. He has continued with a healthy diet, exercise program and basic Body Chemistry Support. In a few months, he will be 60 years of age. In an email he sent me today he stated, "I haven't been sick one day in the past 18 months, and I feel much the same as I did when I was in my late twenties or early thirties."

My big brother has joined the ranks of those who know that we really can *End Illness Now!*

I am honored to have two very professional, dedicated health coaches working in my front office. I asked them both to write brief notes expressing the reasons for their dedication to the work they do.

Janice Gaski wrote:

"I began working for InnerActive Nutrition four years ago. I believed at the time I had a basic understanding of what health was. I had kept my weight down, exercised, and lived a fairly structured life. Being introduced to the Body Chemistry Support System was a new experience for me. I immediately jumped in 100%. Today I feel great! I am more in touch with who I am as a person than I ever have been. I no longer suffer from symptoms of congestion, dehydration, and poor nutrition. These symptoms consisted of mood swings, headaches, back pain, fatigue, and a few others, all of which no longer exist.

I love where my life is today and am so thankful for the opportunity to learn the principles of health that Dr. Mick teaches. He has added so much to my life and I am really living it. I am most thankful for the calmness and clarity about my future health and happiness. I have the knowledge that my body is doing what it was designed to do: heal, love, and cherish this life every day."

Rebecca Clarkson wrote:

"The first cleanse I did with Dr. Mick was approximately sixteen years ago. As the story goes with the fox chasing the rabbit: the fox is running for his dinner—the rabbit is running for his life! As a rabbit, I was only conscious three to four hours a day, struggling with chronic fatigue and fibromyalgia. The mental and physical pain were extremely debilitating. The medical doctors said I had a disease and should learn to live with it, which meant that I must just endure my condition while preparing to die. Instead, I dedicated the next fifteen months to following Dr. Mick's program. After applying the same principles I now coach others to follow, I was able to return to the real world.

After completing the 30-Day Challenge this month for the second time, I was absolutely amazed at how quickly and easily health can now be restored and maintained with the system we offer.

As I now understand, when I was very ill, it was essential that I began by restoring myself physically. This opened the way for me to restore my mental, spiritual and emotional balance. The body has the wisdom to do this on its own if we cooperate with it by simply providing the body chemistry support it needs. I feel the availability of The Body Chemistry Support System is not only a choice, but a real privilege. We are given the tools for Life as it was meant to be! Thank you Dr. Hall for this opportunity to do What Makes My Heart Sing!"

The following are three short stories of experiences I thought you might like...

One day toward the end of the **30-Day Life Restoration Challenge**, a 63-year-old woman was feeling the spontaneous joy of childhood racing through her body. Her immediate response was to just take off running through the hallway leading into her office. As she zipped into her office a worried co-worker asked, "Was that you running through the hallway?" Olgie answered with a little embarrassment and hesitation: "yes." "Are you OK?" "Was there a problem?" The woman continued. "No, I just felt like running," Olgie assured her. *(Olgie S)*

"I have always been quite healthy, but a few months ago I began to realize that my vitality was lower than I was accustomed to. My low vitality, along with an agitating hormone imbalance and a couple of other symptoms, motivated me to visit Dr. Mick. Dr. Mick said that he thought I would find the solutions I was looking for by following the 30-Day Life Restoration Challenge.

By doing the 30-Day Challenge, *all* of my physical symptoms totally reversed, and my vitality went up so high, I felt like a bridge between a higher world and this one. Repeatedly I found myself on my knees on the floor in tears of absolute gratitude— my state of being so balanced, clear and higher than I've ever known. At work, during the busiest time of the year, nothing fazed me. I was happy, balanced and joyful. Moment by moment I was very spiritually connected.

I've **never** felt that good—even as a child. My intuition was 'on' all the time, and my clarity amazing. I don't know of a more profound and stunning gift." *(Jan D.)*

"I didn't have my first eye exam until I was in the second grade. Turns out I had progressive myopia (near-sightedness). All my life, up to that point, everything was blurry and I didn't even know it. That was normal. I'll never forget what it was like the first week I got my glasses. I remember going to church and truly seeing the stained glass windows for the very first time. I was actually brought to tears when I realized how beautiful things really were. When I started with the Body Chemistry Support System, I had no idea how blurry my health was. So, how could I know what it would feel like to be healthy? There was no way. I can tell you this though—just like I'd never go back to being half-blind, I'll never go back to being just half-alive." *(Jim W.)*

Just like I'd never go back
to being half-blind, I'll never
go back to being just
half alive. (Jim W.)

CHAPTER 6

I'm Basically Healthy…So Why Do I Have This Feeling That Something Just Isn't Quite Right?

When a person with a physical problem, which hasn't yet developed into a diagnosable condition, visits a medical doctor, he can sometimes cause as much frustration to the doctor as the doctor's findings cause the individual. A large gray area exists between a person not feeling well and the actual development of a diagnosable symptom or disease. This undefined gray area is referred to by the medical world as *"clinically insignificant,"* because the condition is not yet diagnosable. The individual obviously didn't consider that the way he felt was insignificant, or he would never have taken the time, effort and expense to be evaluated in the first place.

I believe it would be more open and honest if we were told up front the true purpose of the medical industry. The medical industry is a business just like a grocery store or auto repair shop. We have fabricated a perception of the medical industry as being something different than it really is, mostly through the influences of television and our own imaginations.

We watched Dr. Baker on *Little House On The Prairie*, living the life of a monk, making everyone's well-being his personal responsibility. And *Dr. Quinn: Medicine Woman* was always willing to risk her life, and everything of value in it, to save another human from a life-threatening illness or physical trauma. Dr. Welby, Dr. Kildare and so many others have created the image of a medical doctor as an extension of Mother, ready and willing to be at everyone's beck and call to take full responsibility for everyone's well-being and to be sure that, whatever problem a person is having, it is taken care of as quickly as possible.

What a wonderful fairy tale, but when are we going to admit to ourselves that it is no more real than the rabbit with the chocolate eggs and the tooth fairy with all her quarters?

The condition of a person's body is no more the responsibility of a medical doctor than the condition of a person's car is the mechanic's responsibility. Both professionals are in business to eliminate the symptoms that cause your car or body to run improperly. So, the orthodox training of a medical doctor is for the purpose of diagnosing symptoms and diseases, then providing a treatment protocol determined by the pharmaceutical industry.

Who is responsible for the condition of our bodies and the quality of our lives? You guessed it: **we are**.

After decades of studying the body chemistries of thousands of individuals, I made some shocking discoveries. You may find them a little difficult to believe, but I assure you that what I'm about to present to you is very real.

The following nine conditions are consistently found in the bodies of average "healthy adults," not just among those with a diagnosable condition:

- The colon has at least one stricture (constriction, or narrowing of a body passage), causing the recycling of toxic waste into the lymphatic and circulatory systems.
- The intestinal flora is destroyed and out of balance due to the widespread use of chlorinated water and antibiotics. This, along with a strictured colon, causes the production of additional toxins. These additional toxins add to the poisoned condition within the colon that then poisons the blood (our fueling system) and lymph 24 hours a day. This poisoning of the blood and lymph is the number one cause of fatigue and the breakdown of the immune system.
- The colon has a thick, black, rubbery mucus lining developed to protect the lymph and blood as much as possible from the contents of the colon.

- The first stage of scurvy (a vitamin C deficiency) is well established, causing lesions in the arteries and a relatively heavy build-up of arterial plaque, establishing the first stage of circulatory disorders and heart disease, as well as the foundation for stroke.
- The bloodstream is loaded with fungi, chemicals, metals and unusable food waste.
- The gallbladder is stretched and overloaded with cholesterol balls. It is commonly found to be two or three times its normal size. This is a major cause of liver congestion.
- The upper cervical vertebrae are misaligned or the skull is pivoted on the spine, or both.
- Eight round muscles located in the back of the neck, down the center of the back and at the lumbar level of the spine are at least in mild spasm, contracting the spine and causing nerve flow restriction to the associated organs.
- There are also many effects of our commonly over-stressed lifestyles, such as the reduced functions of over-stressed adrenal and thyroid glands, a stress-induced slow rate of metabolism, the reduced efficiency of several energy production systems due to stress-induced deficiencies of essential minerals and other vital nutrients.

Remember, the above problems are the norm for the average "healthy adult," even if he is not yet experiencing discomfort. All internal conditions are worse for those with symptoms, and far worse for anyone with a diagnosable disease. The sad news is that there isn't a pill or a doctor in the world to fix all these problems.

The only solution is for each person to learn how he or she developed this internal environment, and what to do to reverse the condition.

Each person must learn
how he or she developed a
toxic internal environment,
and what to do to reverse
the condition.

CHAPTER 7

Degenerative Disease Doesn't Just Happen: We Create It

Of all the information that could be presented in a book about health, the most valuable (if it were available) would be an explanation of why the human body breaks down and develops disease.

Most books have great descriptions of what is experienced when a person is suffering with a specific condition, and there are usually some good suggestions about what others have done to find relief when they were dealing with such a condition. However, in most cases, the answer to why the condition developed in the first place is still consigned to the world of mysteries.

Before presenting the true reasons why the human body breaks down into every form of degeneration, I would like to first address two very common misconceptions and their associated clarifications:

Misconception #1: The body operates quite similarly to a computer: when it "catches a virus" it will either crash or malfunction for as long as the virus is in the system. Such external influences cause the body to perform strange functions outside of its original programming, such as over-producing cholesterol. Another example of the body's dysfunction is when the immune system sometimes turns on and attacks itself.

Truth: The human body is the epitome of design brilliance. It is the most advanced self-repairing instrument on earth. In every case where it appears that the body is malfunctioning, a deeper, more intelligent review discloses the problem to be an incorrect opinion imposed upon the body by an individual or group who gained financially by publicizing their opinion. The body is always brilliantly doing everything in its power to nor-malize its natural functions. The problem is always with the self-destructive nature of the individual destroying the body faster than it is capable of repairing itself.

Misconception #2: *Disease is an external force continually at-tacking the body in a never-ending attempt to fulfill its purpose of undermining and eventually destroying the human body.*

Truth: Disease is the natural result of exact and predictable causes. The functions of the human body are perfectly regu-lated by the same universal laws that regulate every other liv-ing organism on earth. When any living organism is deprived of vital nutrients, it becomes weak and begins to die. When the life force of any living organism is diminished to a certain level, internal micro-organisms, as well as microorganisms from the environment, assist the dying organism's movement into the next natural phase of the "circle of life" by preparing it to re-turn to the soil of earth as organic matter.

What I will present to you in the next three chapters is so far from what is generally taught in the world of health and disease that your first inclination may be to discard it as just some odd theory. Yet, as different as it may appear, I can assure you that your own intuition will validate these truths for you, as it has, over the years, already attempted to communicate much of this information to you.

The human body is the
epitome of design brilliance.
It is the most advanced
self-repairing instrument
on earth.

CHAPTER 8

The One Major Cause Of All Degenerative Disease

For thousands of years, healers, herbalists, and doctors have effectively and efficiently worked to bring relief to those who suffer from the ills and discomforts that befall mankind. Due to the habitual focus of both the doctor and the individual in need of relief, the field of "doctoring and the doctored" has produced a common desire for quicker and better ways of bringing relief to the sufferer.

In the race to find a faster way of bringing relief to suffering humanity, the principle of cause and effect regarding the health of the human body has been forgotten. The focus on discovering better solutions for the relief of illness has been so intense that questioning cause has been overlooked.

In the United States we have moved past the obvious diseases caused by extreme nutritional deficiency, and past the tragic period of sanitation and germ-related diseases, but we are now engaged in an epidemic that demands the education and personal involvement of every person who wishes to stop this destructive force in his or her life.

The educational starting point must be a thorough understanding of the **One Major Universal Cause Of All Disease: Emotional Trauma.**

I know, at first it might seem to be a bit of a stretch, linking emotional trauma with a distortion of body chemistry, but I can assure you that you are already aware of this link.

In order to create a full picture of how emotional trauma has established itself as the one major universal cause of all disease, I will begin by describing how the body functions as a communication mechanism. You might say that I want to explain "true body language."

As a communication mechanism, the physical body is the external expression of how we feel inside the body. Of course, most of us get a little confused when it comes to identifying exactly who we are. Therefore, I would like to fast-forward a human being to the end of his life, that is, to the experience we refer to as "death." At this point, it immediately becomes very clear who we really are and who we aren't. We recognize that we are the life force that animates the physical body and that, at the time of death, we leave the body life-less. At that point we clearly see the separation of the mind/soul essence from the body/brain/ego vehicle we were temporarily using to experience earth-life.

So, with a clear image in our minds of the difference between who we really are and who we have believed ourselves to be, the fact that we sometimes feel emotional conflicts from within begins to make more sense.

Two extreme forces in our world are directly responsible for everything we experience on earth. They are expansiveness and contractiveness. Every function and every accomplishment in our lives is the direct result of the interplay of these two forces. Peace and harmony are the resulting experiences when a balance has been created between expansiveness and contractiveness. The beating of the human heart is a perfect example of the harmonious balance between expansiveness and contractiveness.

You could say that the interplay between expansiveness and contractiveness is the secret that makes life within the human body possible. Both expressions are essential in order for movement, function and, thereby, for life to exist. The muscular contractions within the stomach and the intestinal tract are another example of the necessity of muscle groups working together, contracting and expanding in order to move our digesting food through the intestines so the nutrients can be delivered into the bloodstream.

The essence of life is the power of expansiveness, while the temporary withdrawal of life results in contractiveness.
The ultimate principle in existence is the principle of expansiveness, or the essence of life, the totality of which we commonly refer to as God, the Omnipotent Omnipresence (All Powerful, Total Presence).

Within the principle of expansiveness and contractiveness is found all the expressions of life and the associated temporary diminishing of life, such as: light and darkness, hot and cold, summer and winter, physical life and physical death.

With this knowledge, it now becomes very easy to understand why the starting point for every form of disease is in the area of the body where the essence of life has been withdrawn or squeezed out by the contractiveness of fear.

Emotional trauma is the direct and immediate cause for the human response of "fear." Fear is the universal expression of contractiveness. Therefore, wherever we hold fear in the body, the tissues of that area contract.

Fear alone is a minor form of contractiveness but, as fear is accumulated or suppressed, it crystallizes into the more destructive forms of contractiveness referred to as stress or anger. Stress is the direct and immediate cause of all disease, because stress causes the long-term contractiveness that literally squeezes the life essence out of the affected area. In any area devoid of the expansiveness of life, disease is a completely natural result!

To clarify any confusion: yes, I did state that "Trauma is the One Major Universal Cause Of All Disease," but, as we view trauma on the scale of cause and effect, we see that emotional trauma is the major cause, activating the contractive expression of fear, which then accumulates and evolves into what we identify as stress. This just means that trauma is the grandfather of stress, as well as the true originator.

Stress is the direct and immediate cause of disease. Stress is a more long-term effect of contractiveness; therefore, in those places where stress is held in the body, the affected body tissues are more permanently contracted, thereby restricting the flow of life through that area.

As you will recall, there are five major pathways through which the substances and essence of life flows throughout the body. These are the bloodstream, the lymphatic system, the intestinal tract, the nervous system, and the meridians. It is easiest to picture these pathways as groups of tubes where these substances and essence flow.

When stress contracts and restricts the flow of life from any one or more of these pathways, the first stage of disease becomes established.

In time, as stress continues to reduce the flow of life through the restricted pathways, the physical substance that disease is made of begins to accumulate and further block the pathways. In time, just like the kinking of a hose, from the point of blockage or partial blockage back to the source of the flow, there will be an increase in pressure. From the point of the blockage to the end of the pathway, there will be a reduction in pressure, or a deficiency of the substance flowing through the pathway. Then, at the point of the blockage, a "tumor" or some other manifestation of the blockage can develop.

Later on there will be a more complete explanation of why most pathways throughout the body are so saturated with the substance of which degenerative disease is made. In the meantime, here is a list of the components of this substance:

- Unusable food residue;
- Dead tissue cells;
- Toxic chemicals;
- Toxic metals;
- The waste by-products of normal cellular function;
- The waste material generated by the presence of parasites and other unfriendly microorganisms.

All together, the saturation and stagnation of these materials throughout the body creates the foundation of all forms of disease.

There is one other way in which stress is well established as the major cause of all disease—that is how stress distorts the tissue mineral levels and the ratios between these minerals.

In order to make perfect sense of the previous statement, let's review the powerful role minerals play in our lives.

Enzymes are like the little worker bees throughout our bodies. All work that gets accomplished does so because of enzymes. They are like the immediate life force, the vital spark that makes things happen. As essential as these little sparks of life are, without minerals, enzymes couldn't even be activated.

We all know how "vital" vitamins are. Without minerals, vitamins are useless.

When we consider the function of every gland and organ in the body, it is essential that we understand the relationship of minerals to this function. It is the ratios between the minerals within the tissues of the body that regulate the function of every gland and organ in the body.

This is probably one of the greatest "curve balls" in the field of nutrition. It is an issue not generally understood in the world of nutrition, but essential for the understanding of hormone balance and the proper functioning of every gland and organ in the body!

By far, one of the most important principles of nutrition that must be understood is how and what determines the tissue level of minerals, and the ratios between these minerals.

A few of these key mineral levels are determined by nutritional intake. A few are determined by toxic exposure. A few mineral levels are distorted because of the intake of white sugar. But the major mineral levels and ratios that determine the function of our glands and organs are regulated by **our emotions**!

That thought deserves a few seconds for pondering, as it is by far the most important health principle that must be understood.

This means, because of the mineral link between our emotions and the function of every gland and organ in our bodies, we **indirectly** control the function of every gland and organ **by our emotional states**.

If we were able to live our lives in a constant state of joy, the major minerals that regulate our glands and organs would naturally establish a proper balance. This being our natural state of being, our overall health would naturally be established in a state of balance.

It should now be very clear that, to the degree we react to the stressors in our lives, we distort our mineral ratios, and thereby distort gland and organ function.

Therefore, it only makes sense that, if we want our glands and organs to function as they were brilliantly designed to do, we must understand well and be diligent in following the instructions in Chapter 27 for healing the traumas responsible for the stress in our lives.

Each of us indirectly controls
the function of every gland
and organ in our bodies by
our emotional states.

CHAPTER 9

The Physical Cause Behind
Degenerative Disease

The brain and nervous system of the human body comprise the most advanced communication system in existence. Our fantastic worldwide telecommunications system is becoming a close copy of the brilliant communication system that is installed into every human body.

As long as the flow of communication from the brain to every part of the body is uninterrupted, and as long as everything else is in order, the body will be strong and function well. But as soon as the nerve flow to any part of the body is interrupted and restricted, the area being starved for nerve flow immediately begins to grow weaker. Once an area becomes weakened, it is no longer capable of properly cleansing itself of the acid debris produced by the local cells. Since the bloodstream usually contains a certain volume of chemicals and metals, any weakened area soon becomes a dumping ground for the excess waste the liver isn't able to remove from the blood. In time, the area of weakness also falls prey to the ill effects of microorganisms that find this weakened, toxic area the perfect place to dine and reproduce.

Total body communication begins in the brain and extends down the spinal cord, branching out from the spinal cord through individual nerves to every part of the body. The most vulnerable point in this system is the passageway down through the core of the first two vertebrae of the neck. In this area of the spinal cord, the nerves are like a bundle of thousands of soft telephone wires. Any pressure against these nerves will reduce or stop the flow of communication to the part of the body these specific nerves are designed to serve.

The two upper cervical vertebrae of the neck are called the atlas and the axis. I refer to their misalignment as being the physical cause of disease in the human body because this misalignment causes constant pressure on the delicate nerves and reduces the flow of communication to important areas of the body. The weakness that results in the body from this major nerve flow interruption is, I repeat, *the physical cause of disease in the human body!*

As we established in the previous chapter, there is one major cause of all degenerative disease. The misalignment of the upper cervical vertebrae is a lesser cause, yet still a cause. Compounding that are nine strong influences, which we will be reviewing in the next chapter, that contribute to the development of all forms of illness.

The most common cause for the misalignment of the upper cervical vertebrae is the assisted birth. At the time of birth, the bones in a baby's neck haven't yet completely formed. Therefore, these bones are more like firm cartilage than hard bones.

The natural way for a human mother to give birth to her baby is to squat. By squatting during her contractions, the weight of the baby assists in dilating the mother's cervix as well as moving the baby more comfortably out of the womb.

When a mother is forced to lie on her back during labor and delivery, the muscular contractions not only have to lift the weight of the baby up the slope of the sacrum and coccyx, but also contract hard enough to push the baby's head to dilate the mother's cervix. All this effort usually requires more energy than a mother has available. No wonder it appears as though a mother is incapable of performing such a natural procedure unassisted.

When the baby's head is pulled and twisted during birth, the skull either gets pivoted on the spine or the first two vertebrae of the neck get misaligned, or both, in every case. This does not even take into consideration the obvious emotional trauma to the baby. This establishes the *physical cause of disease.*

It would be a near miracle if babies could make it to adult-hood without bumping their heads hard enough to misalign their upper cervical vertebrae. Since most upper cervical verte-brae are misaligned from birth, each time there is another ac-cident involving the head, it only agitates and compounds the original misalignment. Even without an assisted birth, how many times does a child learning to walk bump his head? How many times do children fall off bicycles, horses, fences, trees and the many other things children climb on? Then there are accidents while playing, wrestling with other kids, playing con-tact sports and, finally—as children make the transition into adulthood—inevitable automobile accidents. This is why I say that, from the time of birth, it would be a near miracle if a baby could make it to adulthood without bumping his head hard enough to misalign the upper cervical vertebrae. It should now make more sense when I say that this common physical cause is well established in every adult.

When a misalignment of the upper cervical vertebrae exists, specific muscles of the neck have to work harder to compensate for the imbalance caused by the misalignment. In time, these muscles become and remain in spasm. A muscle in spasm refers to any muscle that has been forced into a compensatory state because another area of the body has been injured or (as with the neck) misaligned. In time, the overworked muscle builds up an excess of lactic acid and calcium, which force potassium from the tissue. The condition of the muscle is then forced into perpetual tightness, incapable of relaxing itself. Every muscle in the body that is in spasm further reduces nerve flow to tissue cells. The tight lower back muscles are perfect ex-amples.

An extremely delicate energetic balance naturally flows up and down the spine between the cranium and the sacrum. Any distortion at either end of the spine naturally interrupts this delicate balance and, thereby, creates tension at the opposite end of the spine. The most common result of the misalignment of the upper cervical vertebrae is that, in time, the muscles of the neck will go into spasm. This creates tension in the lower back, which reduces the nerve flow to the colon, which causes a stricture— or a closing down—of the colon. This causes the recycling of toxic waste throughout the body by way of the bloodstream, which is the foundation of all self-poisoning, fatigue, and the breakdown of the immune system. This also causes the greatest volume of the substance of which degenerative disease is made to saturate the entire body, especially any areas of weakness.

Although this seems to be quite a complex chain reaction, without a clear understanding of this chain of events, the logical and systematic self-poisoning of the body would continue as though it were a real mystery, which it isn't.

Before leaving this area of thought, I would like to mention another very strong negative influence regarding the nerve flow restriction from the upper cervical vertebrae. As the tension is transferred up and down the spine, remember how small branches from the spinal cord extend out from the vertebrae and supply communication to every area of the body. When the muscles along the spine are in spasm, it reduces the nerve flow to the vital areas of the body, much the way a dimmer switch works. The more long-term the muscle spasms are, the lower the dimmer switch is turned down, and the more the function of the associated organ is reduced.

I hope the information presented in this chapter has made it clear how essential it is for every person to seek the assistance of a competent chiropractor. The time will come within the reversal process when it will be necessary to seek professional help to assist you in making this vital correction.

When you clearly understand
cause, then correct it, the
body will handle the details for
reversing and clearing the effects.

CHAPTER 10

The Nine Strongest Influences That Destroy The Health Of The Body

This section will provide you with something that has never before in the history of the world been accomplished: the presentation, all together, of the exact reasons the human body breaks down in every form of disease!

So far, we have discussed the two causes for disease:

- The one major cause of all degenerative disease—trauma.
- The physical cause of disease—misaligned upper cervical vertebrae.

Now, to complete the puzzle of cause for why the human body breaks down in all forms of disease, we need to discuss **The Nine Strongest Influences That Destroy The Health Of The Body**. Beyond the two causes and the nine influences, all other reasons for the breakdown of the body fall under the category of effect, not cause. A great example of this is the fact that we have been led to believe that germs are a major cause of disease. Now that we are wiser, we need to re-think such foolishness from the past, and remember that microorganisms feed upon dead plant and animal tissue. Scientists have conducted enough experiments to prove conclusively that, if the energy level of a plant or animal is maintained at a high enough level, it is impossible for an excess of unfriendly microorganisms to live on or in plants or humans. Therefore, if we correct the reasons for diminished life within every area of the body and eliminate the rotting food waste that supports the reproduction of unfriendly microorganisms, germs will no longer play a role in the equation of disease. When this is properly understood, it will become obvious that responsible education is required so that, hopefully, the administering of antibiotics will fall into disuse.

It has been assumed, due to common beliefs within society, that a few of the nine influences listed here are causal in the development of disease. The problem with this belief is that, when you correct a true cause, the effect will clear or be eliminated. However, an *influence* isn't causal. When you correct an influence, there will be a similar level of relief and improvement only to the degree the influence was destructive. Therefore, I have listed the **Nine Destructive Influences** below, not as causes of disease but as strong influences that compound the two causes. In addition, they also create some very strong experiences of discomfort in the body.

The Nine Strongest Influences That Destroy The Health Of The Body, along with their most immediate effects:

1) **Poor selection and destructive preparation of food** (over-cooking food, boiling in oil, using microwaves, etc.) starves the tissue cells and the body chemistry of vital nutrients and food enzymes. It also wastes vital metabolic enzymes and life energy.

2) **Poor digestion** is another cause of nutritional deficiencies and one of the two main causes of poor elimination, as undigested food stagnates in the intestinal tract instead of supplying nutrients to the bloodstream.

3) **Poor elimination** is the main cause of autointoxication (self-poisoning). It is the most common cause of fatigue. It is the major cause for the breakdown of the immune system and congestion of the liver. It also provides the waste that physically clogs the pathways throughout the body where life is meant to flow.

4) **Dehydration** is one of the three main causes of tissue destruction, along with autointoxication and free radical destruction. Dehydration also distorts body chemistry, and allows for the stagnation of poisons throughout the body.

5) **Nerve flow restriction** always interferes with the communication from the brain to the affected area of the body.

It is the direct cause of weakness developing in an affected area, which then allows an ideal place for disease to develop.

6) **Exposure to toxic substances** damages tissue cells, especially delicate glandular cells. It also adds to the substance within the body that clogs the pathways of life, the same substance degenerative disease is actually comprised of.

7) **Inactive lifestyle** inhibits the release of toxic waste from the tissues of the body, allowing stagnation and a direct poisoning of tissue cells. Since movement stimulates life, a lack of movement interferes with the natural delivery of nutrients at the cellular level and, therefore, allows cellular deficiencies of nutrients and oxygen, thereby reducing and destroying energy production.

8) **Accidents** are the main cause of adult spinal misalignments, which interfere with the proper nerve flow from the brain to every area of the body. Accidents also cause other direct body damage to glands, organs and tissues. Accidents cause a great deal of physical as well as emotional stress, which creates an excess build-up of calcium in stressed areas of the body, which sedates function and creates irritating calcium deposits.

9) **Surgery** creates excess trauma and scar tissue. It can destroy nerve flow, thereby diminishing the associated body functions. Anesthesia disrupts brain and hormonal functions; and most areas of the body, after undergoing surgical interference, lose their capacity for normalizing natural functions.

Considering these eleven major reasons (two causes and nine influences) for the breakdown of the human body, it is clear that we can never expect to hear of an honest "cure" for any degenerative disease. Since there isn't one single *cause* for the development of degenerative disease, there can never be one single *solution*.

In our world of cause and effect, correcting cause and reversing the negative influences will always be the only way to permanently eliminate the effects we refer to as *the symptoms of disease.*

I would like to share a few thoughts on each of the nine influences listed above, just to unite them with some practical application to our lives.

1) Poor selection and destructive preparation of food: Years ago I read of an experiment that clearly demonstrated a major reason for the compromised health of Americans. Scientists observed two groups of dogs. The first group was given all the water they wanted for a month, but no food. At the end of the month, they were found to be in excellent health. The scientists observed a second group of dogs that were also given all the water they wanted, but were also allowed to eat whatever quantity of white bread they wanted. Within two weeks, the white bread had literally fatigued the second group of dogs to death.

The white bread, having no food value and requiring such a large amount of energy to digest and eliminate its bulk, created such an energy deficit that it killed the dogs within a two-week period.

It's good to remember that white bread isn't the only foodless food causing such fatigue in the United States. All foods made with white flour, white rice, white sugar or any other highly processed food items have had their life-giving properties destroyed and their nutrients removed. It is for this reason that the body will respond to such foods as a wood stove filled with water-soaked newspapers would.

2) Poor digestion: The enzymes used for digesting our food could be considered very tiny energy packets, like microscopic flashlight batteries. In this example, the battery represents a protein molecule and enzymes are represented by the energy in the battery.

Energy, life force, enzymes, it's all the same. The difference is your application. For example, you could plug a radio into your bedroom outlet and use electric energy to produce music. You could use the same electric current flowing into your kitchen to bake a loaf of bread. Energy is energy. Our application of the energy is what determines the work the energy accomplishes.

Cooking food destroys its life, or energy. When we cheat ourselves out of this vital source of energy by eating too much cooked food, we suffer in many ways. The first way is by having to sacrifice our own life force by converting our metabolic enzymes into digestive enzymes to digest the cooked food, as was the fate of the dogs in the experiment described above.

Another common practice for adults is to addictively convert every available trace of energy into accomplishments. Comparing energy to money, most adults are energetically bankrupt! Give an adult a unit of energy and, rather than enjoying the increased life in his body, he'll turn around and convert it into an accomplishment as quickly as possible. All our lives we have been given the choice between life and accomplishment. Most of us have continually chosen accomplishment and now stand in wonder at the depletion of our life energy.

This is why poor digestion is so common. If there isn't enough energy for the body to heal itself, and to function as it was designed, how can it take from such a limited supply of energy and produce digestive enzymes to digest food? This is why drinking vegetable juice and consuming raw fruits, vegetables and sprouted nuts, seeds and grains is so helpful in restoring the life essence we have already used up.

3) **Poor elimination:** Poor elimination is a combination of several causal influences. It begins with the childhood response to fear. A child's response to fear is generally to hold contractiveness in the abdominal area. This basic beginning is compounded by the consumption of sticky white flour products as well as pasteurized dairy products and other sticky foods. Making matters worse is the use of chlorinated water and antibiotics,

both of which destroy the friendly intestinal bacteria and cause further stagnation, stickiness and constipation. In time, the constipated colon creates contractiveness within the lower back. This further reduces the nerve flow from the spinal cord to the colon, creating a stricture (a closing down of the colon), which causes abdominal distention and chronic constipation. As you will recall, this is the main cause of autointoxication.

4) **Dehydration:** Have you ever noticed the parallel that exists between a human transitioning from youth into old age and a grape transitioning into a raisin? The common principle creating the transition is dehydration. Dehydration is the result of many things, but the most direct shortcut to dehydration is the drinking of dehydrating substances like coffee, soda pop and alcohol. The next most obvious is *not* drinking plenty of water every day. The third shortcut to dehydration is over-exposure to the sun. Because dehydration is so serious, we need to expand on the points presented earlier.

- When the lymph is thickened by dehydration and incapable of washing the acid waste away from the tissue cells, the cells are rapidly destroyed, thereby greatly intensifying the aging process and degeneration.
- With the increased destruction of tissue cells comes an increase in free radical destruction.
- Even in a mild state of dehydration, the body is inhibited in delivering nutrients to the cells to maintain normal function.
- Dehydration inhibits the proper electron flow, and thereby reduces energy production not only among the cells, but also with the transfer of energy throughout the body. This causes a depression of energy and an irritation of the entire nervous system, resulting in everything from insomnia to rage.

5) **Nerve Flow Restriction:** We covered in detail the most extreme example of nerve flow restriction in our discussion of the misalignment of the upper cervical vertebrae. The example

of my brother Jeff's experience from Chapter 1 is an extreme example of the paralyzing effect of nerve flow restriction. Jeff's spinal cord wasn't damaged, it only had the pressure of the misaligned atlas and axis vertebrae pressing on both sides of it at the same time, restricting communication to such a degree that he experienced total loss of mobility from the neck down. Although Jeff was paralyzed and not able to move any part of his body below his neck, his autonomic nervous system sustained the vital life functions of his body. When Dr. White realigned his vertebrae and allowed the nerve flow to be restored down through the spinal cord, Jeff slowly regained the movement of his entire body.

Another example of nerve flow restriction is the condition of the colon described at the end of influence #3, Poor Elimination (in this section); then add a few more years, along with a further decrease in the nerve flow from the lower back. This lays the foundation for all the serious colon conditions such as Crohn's disease, irritable bowel syndrome, colitis, bowel polyps, hemorrhoids, and colon cancer.

6) **Exposure to toxic substances:** From the time of childhood we have been heavily saturated with toxic chemicals and metals without being informed of their destructive effects on our bodies. The water we drank was always loaded with chlorine, which destroyed the friendly bacteria of our intestinal tracts. Our eggs, milk, chicken and beef were loaded with antibiotics. Added to this were the generous helpings of antibiotics we were given by our doctors (often indiscriminately). These factors served to not only complete the destruction of our intestinal flora, but also to assist us in developing a new hybrid race of unfriendly microorganisms incubating within our intestinal tracts.

In addition, for the sake of profits and for fear of lawsuits, the dental associations (over the past two or three decades) have encouraged our dentists to be dishonest with us about the toxic effects of mercury fillings. All along, dentists have been given strict instructions for the proper handling and disposal of this highly toxic material we have been paying them to put into our mouths.

Another area of concern is the thousands of chemicals hiding in our food supply. If we knew the accumulative effects of the chemicals the food industry puts into our food for their financial benefits, we would definitely select the foods we eat much more carefully.

And, finally, we know that every pharmaceutical preparation we have ever used has many toxic side effects. Have you ever stopped to think about how destructive the accumulative drug deposits can become that are being trapped within your body?

7) **Inactive lifestyle:** In a septic system there are several drain lines leading away from the septic tank, allowing the water from the tank to be drained and soak into the soil. Without these drain lines, the tank would just fill up and have to be pumped out almost weekly. Our lymphatic system works in a similar manner to remove the acid waste from around our tissue cells. The problem with our lymph, though, is that most of it has to move uphill, and fluids don't flow uphill. Therefore, the design of the lymphatic system is such that it utilizes a system of vessels with many one-way valves. Since there is no pumping mechanism to move the lymph uphill, the lymphatic system relies on our deep breathing and movement. When we are active, our breathing and muscular contractions, along with bending, climbing stairs and all healthy movement, keep our lymph flowing and our tissues clean and healthy. On the other hand, to the degree that we just sit in one place and remain inactive, our lymph stagnates. In time, an inactive lifestyle allows the lymph to stagnate and the body to become septic and poisoned. This is why physical activity is crucial for the normal functioning of the body. This is not just a good idea—it is an essential one.

On the delivery side of our tissue cells, the contraction and expansion of our muscles assist in the delivery of nutrients to our cells. For the length of time we are inactive, our tissue cells become starved for the needed nutrients. One of the most vital nutrients for our cells is oxygen. As long as the body is inactive, our shallow breathing and poor circulation starves the entire body for oxygen. Oxygen is essential for energy production and is nature's greatest purifier. Movement generates life in the body. Stagnation allows disease and death to take over.

8) **Accidents:** Three major effects of accidents set up an ongoing interruption in the body's normal functions, as well as setting up a gradual decline of function. The first is the emotional trauma that is always a part of every accident. The second is the direct tissue destruction. Whether it is organ or glandular damage, or damaged muscle tissue, there will be greater nutritional demands and most likely the development of scar tissue. Scar tissue within the organs, as well as adhesions among the intestines, will tend to inhibit natural functions and create negative influences that can cause further complications.

Along with the emotional trauma, the damage that an accident causes to the spine locks the body into a perpetual tailspin that will continue until both are properly treated.

9) **Surgery:** Most surgeries are like unnecessary self-inflicted accidents. Two of the three destructive results of accidents also apply to surgery. You have the trauma and the scar tissue to deal with, just as though you had an accident. While it is true that an organ that has been removed will never bother you again since it was thrown away, the designer of the human body wouldn't agree with your doctor that the part was unnecessary. My advice, of course, would be for you to listen to the intuitive warnings about your destructive lifestyle that persisted long before surgery was suggested. Follow your intuitive promptings for reopening the nerve flow to the affected area. Then, detoxify that part of your body so that it can restore its natural function.

Besides the individual symptoms that each one of these nine influences can create on its own, it should now be easier to understand how any one or more of these influences, in concert with the two causes, can create every degenerative disease in existence. We really don't need the billions of dollars of research money to continue the witch-hunt for the mysterious "X" factor that causes our diseases. All that is required is for each person to understand the true reasons the body develops all forms of illness, and then take personal responsibility for correcting and reversing these reasons.

We also need to remember that the human body is bound by the same laws of physics as our automobiles are, and that they function with the same logic.

Disease is not some mysterious, external force, always trying to attack and destroy the human body. Disease is an inside job, of which we are the cause, and disease the effect.

When each person discovers that a perfectly healthy body has no need for any form of treatment, we can shift into a whole new paradigm where human suffering is no longer a lucrative source of income for the medical and pharmaceutical industries.

Disease is not some mysterious, external force, always trying to attack and destroy the human body. Disease is an inside job, of which we are the cause, and disease the effect.

CHAPTER 11

Genetic Predisposition

While we're busy cleaning up old false perceptions and beliefs from the past, we may as well bury the outdated perception regarding genetic predisposition.

Genetic predisposition is a popular term that implies that, whatever health condition afflicted one of our parents or grandparents, it is quite probable that we will end up experiencing the same.

Unfortunately, this term is now being used to manipulate individuals into agreeing to medical procedures that, in most cases, are not in the individual's best interest. The following story is a perfect example.

About four years ago I was in England and read a newspaper article about a woman whose mother had died from breast cancer. As a young girl, she was so emotionally devastated by the loss of her mother that now, as a mother herself, she allowed a surgeon to convince her that the perfect preventive medicine would be to have both of her healthy breasts cut off to guarantee that she wouldn't die of breast cancer, thereby saving her daughters from the horrible grief that she went through as a young girl. Being convinced that she owed this to her daughters, the woman consented to having her breasts cut off.

Although her surgeon convinced her that he was providing her with the ultimate solution, the woman will be quite distraught one day to learn the fact that all levels of cause for her to develop cancer are still intact. Although the condition cannot develop in her missing breasts, if the actual causes for why she might have developed breast cancer are not reversed, her body will manifest a condition of cancer in the next most vulnerable area.

When we discuss the levels of cause for breast cancer, it will become clearer that cutting off a woman's breasts is an unnecessary and sad way of attempting to avoid something that was *already* completely avoidable.

In order to understand the truth about genetic predisposition, we first need to delve into the mechanics of the body's cellular functions.

Dr. Bruce Lipton did a great job of clearing up many misunderstandings of how our cells really function in his book, *The Biology of Belief*.

For decades, it was generally accepted that, since the DNA recordings were within the nucleus of every cell, it was only logical for the nucleus to be the "brain" of each cell. Then, after the careful removal of the nucleus from a cell and the monitoring and observation that followed, scientists were amazed to discover that, without the nucleus, the cell continued to function very intelligently. They also observed, however, that if the cell received any damage, it wasn't able to repair itself and, at the end of its life, wasn't able to reproduce itself. The scientists discovered that the nucleus actually functioned as the "gonads" (reproductive organs) of the cell, not the brain.

After the great discovery regarding the nucleus, the membrane of the cell was then studied more closely and was found to be the active transmitting and receiving brain for the cell. So, looking at the bottom line of these discoveries, we see that the memories of all experiences of the body are stored in the cell's "hard drive," the DNA, which is within the nucleus of the cell. We then see that the membrane is actually the active, transmitting, receiving, functioning "brain" of the cell. The membrane is in constant communication with its immediate environment and makes moment-to-moment adjustments to adapt to the ever-changing forces of life.

So what is genetic predisposition, and how much power does it have in the decision-making process of disease?

First, we know that a complete history of the life and experience of our cells is stored in the DNA of every cell in our bodies. In fact, it has been estimated that it would require 1,000 books of 600 pages each to record the history contained in one cell. Now, of the millions of memories stored in the DNA of the cell, which memories do you suppose would distort body function and thereby have a negative influence on the next generation? You guessed it, memories of emotional trauma.

Emotional trauma is generally the result of one of at least three types of experiences. Direct emotional devastation is the most common and obvious form of trauma. The next is the emotional experience that results from a traumatic physical experience. The third might be only a false perception of a traumatic experience, in other words, a non-traumatic experience that was only perceived as being traumatic. Just as beauty is in the eye of the beholder, so is trauma.

As we discussed before, the natural human response to trauma is the contractive response of fear, which eventually evolves and crystallizes into stress. In addition, a few other strong emotions naturally branch off from trauma. They are anger, hate, resentment, and sadness.

A traumatic experience that has the power to "break a person's heart" carries the same power to eventually cause a fatal heart attack. The DNA memory of a broken heart also has the power to reach into the next generation or two and predispose the children and the children's children to "heart disease."

A traumatic experience involving powerful deceit or betrayal can generate enough hate, anger and resentment to lock down a person's liver and cause liver disease, cancer, arthritis or one of the many other diseases that are based in hate, anger or resentment. It also has the power to reach beyond the grave to predispose children and grandchildren to developing similar diseases.

The great news is that genetic predisposition is not dictatorial. It is only suggestive, and it can be reversed. As I hope you are becoming aware, the purpose of this book is to completely remove the mystery behind why the body develops every form of illness, so that you can be freed from all fear associated with every form of disease.

You will know the truth and the truth will set you free from all fear!

You will know the truth
and the truth will set you
free from all fear!

CHAPTER 12

Disease Is No Mystery

A woman drove her car into a local mechanic's shop one day for repairs. She explained to the mechanic the problem she had been having with the car's engine. The mechanic considered the information the woman gave him as he listened to the running engine to determine whether he would be able to solve the problem. After a few minutes, he reported to the woman that the actual reason for the engine problem was a bit of a mystery to him, but, if she would like to leave the car with him, he would open the engine up in a couple of areas and attempt to find the true problem. The woman thanked him but said that she would rather not, and drove on to another shop. As she spoke with a mechanic at the second shop, she repeated exactly what she had told the mechanic at the first shop. The second mechanic listened to the engine and, after a few minutes, told the woman what was wrong, how long it would take to repair the engine and approximately how much it was going to cost.

Why was the engine problem a mystery for the first mechanic? That's right, either a lack of information or a lack of experience.

If we compare human disease with ignorance and darkness, there is only one common way to overcome all three, and it is definitely not by fighting them. When the light switch of awareness is flipped on, all darkness, mystery and ignorance are dispelled.

In the preceding five chapters, we discussed the reasons for the breakdown of the human body in all forms of disease. I would now like to bring all the reasons together and demonstrate how the same causal components in various combinations are able to create the many diversified human diseases.

By reducing disease to such simplicity, I hope you will no longer believe in, or support, the concept that the body is such a mysterious instrument that we just can't figure out how to stop it from breaking down and destroying itself. I would also like to make it clear that what we generally call "the natural aging process" is a very *unnatural* way to destroy our bodies and should never be allowed to become debilitating.

When we are born, ideally, we could be considered fully alive. In other words, the life essence that we are is fully present in the body. If we graph this on a simple gradient scale from 0 to 100, our birth would place us at the position of 100 on the graph. The reason I mentioned we could "ideally" be considered to be fully alive at birth is because we need to remember that a baby's newly formed little liver had to filter the toxic waste that its mother's liver wasn't able to remove from *her* blood. The most obvious demonstration of this is a baby with jaundice.

A baby is generally born as an ideal example of health. By the time a baby turns two years of age, it is definitely expressing itself as the epitome of health, being fully alive, totally flexible, and radiating the joy of life.

In time, the harshness of life and the physical and emotional hurts begin to accumulate in the life of this innocent child. A glance at the child's position on the gradient "Scale of Life" indicates a shifting away from the position of 100. The harshness of life unfortunately causes the beginning of the descent toward the 0 point—the point we call death.

By the time this healthy, innocent child reaches the age of six years, the foundation of the human belief system, which is the foundation of **our expectations of life**, is well established. From birth, the two trillion tissue cells of the body all contain the full memory of every traumatic experience of both parents and all four grandparents. Just a note for clarity: although the memories of the 20 or 30 generations preceding the lives of the grandparents are also recorded in the grandparents' DNA, the influence beyond the grandparents isn't as strong. Therefore, for the sake of simplicity, when we refer to the grandparents' DNA, it is with the understanding that every significant trauma from the entire family history before the grandparents is also recorded in their DNA.

Add to this memory foundation about 20,000 of **each** cautionary warning, such as: "don't touch," "no, no," "that will hurt you," "get down before you fall," "that will burn you," and other threatening warnings. By the time a child is six years old, he or she is thoroughly convinced that the world is not a safe place, and that life is ready to hurt you in a myriad of ways. Further, these beliefs are intensified by thousands of traumatic memories inherited from the parents' DNA.

We call this human prep school the "formative years." They are considered the formative years because, by the time we reach six years of age, our expectations of life are well established.

Our personal belief systems determine **our expectations of life**, which in turn dictate the quality of our lives and determine the health of our bodies, the success of our relationships, our financial status, and the flow of good into our lives. Therefore, I believe it is a wise idea to understand the nature of this beast, so that we can learn how to make the necessary corrections at the causal level.

Below is a list of some of the possible negative programming that makes up the belief system of a six-year-old child. As adults, we lose touch with these factors that collectively establish our expectations of life.

1) The thousands of traumatic memories clearly recorded in the DNA of every cell of the body are the true emotional traumas, the emotional effects of physical traumas, and the perceived traumas of the child's two parents and four grandparents.

2) Remember the automatic emotion-duplicating system described in Chapter 4. Because of this system, during the time a baby is in his mother's womb, he experiences

all the fears, stresses and upsets of life right along with his mother.

3) As adults, we have completely forgotten how harsh life seems to a newborn baby and the drama that usually surrounds "the natural birthing process," which makes birth one of the most traumatic experiences of our lives. If the baby hasn't been drugged (by way of the doctor drugging the mother), the baby is generally the most aware individual in the birthing room. When the baby is treated like a thing, and everyone focuses their fears regarding the well-being of the mother and baby on this "thing" being removed from the mother, that only adds to a baby's traumatic experience of birth. If the baby is hurt during or after the birth, this also compounds the traumatic experience. I believe it is important to take some time to view the normal hospital birthing experience from a baby's point of view. Imagine the comfort and security of the baby, curled up in its mother's belly in the ideal waterbed, at the perfect temperature. All needs are automatically met. The baby doesn't even need to breathe for itself. As the time of delivery approaches, the baby begins to feel the stress building because his mother must leave the comfort of home, travel to a strange place and deal with many variable circumstances. All this, on top of feeling extremely uncomfortable. In the old emergency handbooks given to policemen, firemen and other emergency personnel, the instructions for assisting a mother giving birth ended with the reassurance that the assistant wouldn't need to resuscitate the baby because, in an emergency, drugs aren't administered to a mother. Can you imagine the horrible feeling for a very aware baby to suddenly be drugged to such a degree that many have to be resuscitated immediately after birth? Then, at the time of birth, the baby's head is forced to collapse in order to squeeze through the birth canal, which must be terribly

traumatic. When the head is then pulled and twisted, we can be certain that this is traumatic for the baby. Then the baby comes out of a dark place and into a bright delivery room **with eyes that have never been used before**, which is extremely harsh and painful. The frosting on the cake is the rush to put silver nitrate drops into those tender little eyes, followed by the unnecessary scrubbing of the baby's skin. To scrub a newborn's tender skin is no different than using a wire brush and lye soap to scrub an adult. Imagine then the ceremony of strapping the newborn boys down to unnecessarily cut their foreskins off, without even anesthetizing the tissue. I don't know of any adults who would allow others to treat them in this manner. After realizing how a baby is generally welcomed into life, we need not wonder why most of us grow up with cautious expectations of life. The way we perceive life from our very first experiences establishes a huge expectation!

4) From the time of birth, the fears of the parents are projected onto the child in thousands of ways, thoroughly convincing the child that life is a dangerous and scary place to be. The child's DNA, which carries the thousands of traumatic memories from parents and grandparents subtly confirms: *yes, it's true; life will repeatedly hurt you in many ways...*

This foundation is well established by the age of six. Is it any wonder why our expectations of life continue to draw similar circumstances into our lives? Then, every time a traumatic experience is repeated, it more firmly solidifies our expectations.

Now that the one major cause for all degenerative disease has been established, we can formulate the pattern of development for *all* degenerative diseases more clearly.

Obviously, every degenerative disease begins to develop from birth in three ways: the programming of trauma that imposes a **reduced expectation of life** onto the body; the programming of trauma that imposes a **contractive influence** upon the pathways of life throughout the body; and the programming of trauma that imposes a **distortion of the tissue mineral levels** which regulate the function of every gland and organ in the body.

The next common ingredient is the pivot of the skull on the spine or a misalignment of the upper cervical vertebrae of the neck. This direct physical cause reduces the communication from the brain through the nerves to the essential areas of the body allowing weakness to develop and, in time, establishing the area where disease can develop.

With the two causes (trauma and upper cervical misalignment) established in the body from early childhood, and by adding the following Nine Powerful Influences (which were discussed in detail in Chapter 10), all the components necessary for the development of every form of degenerative disease are present:

1) Poor selection and destructive preparation of food.
2) Poor digestion.
3) Poor elimination.
4) Dehydration.
5) Nerve flow restriction.
6) Exposure to toxic substances.
7) Inactive lifestyle.
8) Accidents.
9) Surgeries and the use of toxic anesthetics.

Earlier in this section, we talked about a gradient scale of measurement called the Scale of Life. Of course, all eleven of the reasons for disease constantly diminish the life essence from the body and force the individual down this "Scale Of Life." Cancer is the most obvious example of a person who has moved a great distance down the scale. A person does not just "get cancer." The systemic condition of cancer generally involves the whole body. Although isolated cancers *do* develop, they are only in specific areas where nerve flow, then blood flow, has been seriously restricted. The nerve flow restriction creates a weakened area and the reduced blood flow allows the condition of cellular oxygen starvation to exist, which forces the mutation of the tissue cells in the weakened area.

With the exception of isolated cancers, it takes a long time to create a condition of cancer. A child is sometimes able to create cancer more quickly because of the running head start provided by one or both parents. Other than that, however, it takes a long time for the eleven destructive reasons to create systemic cancer.

By the time a person develops systemic cancer, the life force is approximately 80% gone from the body, the liver is so congested is hasn't been able to properly clean the blood for decades, and the entire lymphatic system is stagnated with the substances of which degenerative disease is made.

As a matter of clarification, there is a difference between what I refer to as systemic cancer and a condition involving an isolated tumor. In either case, there may only be one tumor present in the entire body, but there is a substantial difference between the body chemistry of each. One person, let's say a teen or young adult, can be quite vital; yet, due to the exposure of a highly toxic substance, he or she can develop a cancerous tumor. In such an individual, there is smaller chance of the cancer spreading throughout the body, unless the primary tumor isn't removed within a reasonable time. In what I refer to as a systemic condition, the entire life-force of the body is low, the immune system is low, a great deal of free radical activity is present throughout the body, the intestinal system has been sluggish, and the liver and kidneys haven't been able to keep up with their work load for years. So, as I emphasize throughout this book, it takes a great deal of time and consistency to create a serious degenerative disease. There will be plenty of time and plenty of warnings before something so seriously destructive is created. It never just happens!

When we thoroughly understand the cause of any problem, we can move more quickly toward a solution; but, as long as we are told that the cause is unknown and there is no solution, we struggle on without hope.

My desire is to give hope—not only by describing in detail all levels of cause, but by describing all levels of solution—and provide you with the assurance that thousands of people have been utilizing this information for years and are truly free from the symptoms of degenerative disease and the many fears that accompany every form of degenerative disease.

Knowing that the human body was programmed to be capable of restoring its normal functions when the proper support is provided has been a lighthouse of hope for thousands who were suffering with horrible conditions. These people are now enjoying the fruits of their labors by experiencing what it really means to be healthy.

When we thoroughly understand
the cause of any problem, we
can move more quickly toward
a solution; but, as long as we are
told that the cause is unknown
and there is no solution, we
struggle on without hope.

CHAPTER 13

Set Yourself Free From The Game of Illness

Of all the chapters in this book, this is the one I would ask you to read most thoughtfully and carefully.** The **perspective** I am going to present to you, and from which I will ask you to view this information, is probably more important than the information itself.

I hope you will receive what I'm about to present as a healthy viewpoint of the game you and I have been drawn into without our knowledge and without our consent. It's a game so skillfully interwoven into our lives that we accept it without question as being an integral part of modern life.

Since we were babies, our minds have been conditioned to play "The Game." The scary thing is that behind the kind and helpful mask projected by the game masters is the most powerful, life-threatening, money-generating, machine in history.

Before reading about the Game Of Illness, be sure to stop and really feel the answer to this question: **What form of treatment does a perfectly healthy person require?**

As concerned individuals always working to better the world and improve our personal lives, you and I have a common trait that sometimes allows us to be taken advantage of. We believe that all people are as busy as we are at improving their personal lives and extending that out into the world, so that the world will be a better place because of our combined efforts. Unfortunately, that isn't quite what is happening.

Before we were born, a system was designed. It was like a machine with artificial intelligence and great power but without a conscience. It was called a **Corporation**.

In the hands of good men, a corporation can be a vehicle for generating much good in the world; conversely, in the hands of men with compromised morals and ethics, it can be a curse to the world.

A corporation is a vehicle that allows individuals to hide behind policies and protocol and accomplish things they would never have the "stomach" to do themselves.

This is like having army tanks equipped with cameras and remote controls that would allow a CEO of a corporation to sit in his air-conditioned office and destroy the lives of others in the name of corporate profits, without having to experience the harsh reality of his actions.

A great many large corporations have become shamelessly guilty of destroying people, animals, and the planet for the sake of larger profits. The collective damage these corporations are causing is out of control.

Documentaries are becoming a popular way of educating the public about what is really happening. Please take advantage of the efforts behind these documentaries and view every one you come across; they are the voices of people like you and me who are warning others of the suffering caused for the sake of greed.

I feel obligated to emphasize to you that there are two groups of corporations that have the power to destroy you if you allow them to. One is the processed food industry; the other is the pharmaceutical industry. Of the two, the pharmaceutical industry is by far the more sinister, with far greater destructive capabilities.

These are the two areas where corporate greed has so powerfully dissolved all forms of morality and conscience that the consumer's well-being doesn't even matter. If it will draw money from you and they can get away with it without being imprisoned, then their attitude is, *anything goes.*

I don't condone greed in any form, especially the form of greed that exchanges lives and suffering for money. However, it is vitally important to remember that **greed is supported only by ignorance and apathy.** When we come to know better and when we collectively exercise our commitment to removing our support for greed and wrong action, both will die from lack of support.

As you have probably guessed by now, the number one industry in the United States is the **health care/disease care industry.** It generates an annual income of just under two trillion ($2,000,000,000,000) dollars per year.

If you were invited to play a game that was almost impossible to win, how interested would you be in that game? Before answering too quickly, be sure you consider how many dollars you have already donated into the lottery.

For the past century, a game has been evolving that may not be as impossible to win as the lottery; but, if you play the game, you become a losing part of the greatest income-generating machine in history.

The bottom line of this game is: the people of the United States collectively pay into the game nearly two trillion dollars each year with the hope of achieving the desired result—to live a disease-free life.

Talk about a game where everyone loses and the house wins! Have you considered the statistics lately? There has never been a time in the history of the world when an individual has had a greater chance of dying of some horrible and painful degenerative disease than right now. The time has come for us to stop and re-evaluate our choices and their related outcomes, and consider the possibility of making wiser choices.

It reminds me of the definition of insanity that states: "Insanity is the process of repeating the same action, while hoping for a different result."

I refer to what is happening with disease care today as **The Game of Illness** because the average person is gambling enormous sums of money in the hope of winning his freedom from suffering. Yet, like the games in Vegas, you have many more chances of *losing* your money than winning. It is categorized as a game because others have purposely designed the game to generate huge profits for themselves, while guaranteeing that you only win enough to keep you playing. The sad thing is that your money is not even your greatest loss. The stakes are much higher than that—your pain, suffering, and eventual death.

Now remember, every time you place your bet, **it isn't money you're hoping to win, it's the freedom from suffering.** We place our bets in this game in several ways. An obvious way is through the premiums we (or our employers) pay into a health insurance plan. Then there are the many blood tests, physicals and check-ups, not to mention the medications prescribed to relieve the problems detected by the evaluations. And, of course, there are the many over the counter medications purchased all the time. The greatest volume of money that is going to the designers of the game is taken from us in the form of taxes, and then just handed over on our behalf. One day we are going to be stunned to discover how much we have **involuntarily** paid into this game! Another shocking revelation will come when the truth is finally made public of how many billions of dollars have been donated to fundraisers to find "the cure" for various diseases, **and "the cure" isn't even being looked for**! In fact, to recognize an actual cure or reversal for cancer would be considered a foolish corporate blunder.

Have you ever heard of Dr. Mathias Rath? Dr. Rath is a medical doctor from Germany who was granted a patent for reversing heart disease. Just think about that, a medical doctor who was granted a patent for reversing the most deadly disease in our country.

Here in the United States, the FDA and several other organizations claim to exist for the safety, protection and well-being of the people. Doesn't it make sense that, with such an historic event as a patent being granted for the reversal of the most deadly disease in the United States, these organizations would shout the news from the rooftops? The sad thing is to realize that these organizations are actively and aggressively suppressing this information to protect the financial interests of the pharmaceutical industry, whose members are well integrated into these "government agencies."

Receiving the news that a friend, relative, or acquaintance has died from a drug reaction or mishap in a hospital or doctor's office has become more commonplace in today's world. A careful and accurate research project has recently been completed which revealed that, in 2001, 783,936 people died in this manner. Think about that for a second, we're talking about **nearly eight hundred thousand people in one year, in the United States alone**, who laid down a huge amount of money on a bet that they would be free from suffering and unnecessary death, only to have their lives taken by the very people whom they had entrusted to protect them! The ironic thing is that, since the news media didn't jump on this and tell us that it was bad or wrong, everyone continues as though nothing has happened.

Isn't the power of the media interesting? When a small group of people called "terrorists" killed fewer than 3,000 Americans on 9/11, the news media said this was bad and very wrong. Therefore, most of the people in our country were extremely upset and considered it to be a completely unacceptable attack on the American people as, of course, it was. Yet, another group of people knowingly plays a form of Russian roulette with millions of our family members every year, and cause nearly eight hundred thousand people to lose the game **every year**. The saddest thing about this attack is that we all know it is happening but, since the news reporters don't make the statement that it is wrong, everybody condones it by default as an acceptable loss, or collateral damage!

By the time you finish this book, I hope you know without a doubt that there are much better choices available. You don't have to play "Medical Russian Roulette" and take the chance of being one of the eight hundred thousand people who needlessly dies this year. The reason you don't have to play The Game is because **a perfectly healthy person has no need for any type of treatment!**

The time has come for us to stop fighting disease, stop looking for magic cures that don't exist. In fact, magic cures wouldn't be the solution even if they *did* exist, since they would have no power to support the body in correcting the necessary levels of cause.

It's time to simply learn the principles that determine the health and well-being of the body and follow them, then we won't need to worry about curing anything. That would be the perfect exit door from the game of illness.

Here's just a thought about how much money two trillion dollars is: two trillion dollars could turn two million people into millionaires. Or, better yet, imagine how far **two trillion dollars every year** would go toward correcting the problems mankind has caused our planet.

A perfectly healthy person
has no need for any type
of treatment!

CHAPTER 14

Is Your Doctor Part Of The Solution, Or Part Of The Problem?

As controversial as life sometimes appears, I love it when I come across a thought or a principle that has been distilled to its core of simplicity because, at that level, it has the power to cut through opinions and lay bare the simple truth. This tool was actually given to us from the Bible: "By their fruits you shall know them." You can't find a much simpler scale of measurement than that! By evaluating the results brought about by a person or an organization, you can know the true purpose and intent of the person or organization.

When it comes to evaluating our medical doctors we need to remember that, in the past, we always looked at them from the perspective television, movies and advertisements created for us.

Viewing medical doctors through the images implanted into our minds allows us to be absolutely trusting and accepting. After all, we have been conditioned to see medical doctors as substitute mothers, where the providing of our health care is concerned.

We have all played a role in creating this image. For decades, a belief has been evolving that the person wearing the white coat and stethoscope is the ultimate authority on health. The truth is that medical training doesn't even include instruction in the principles of health, only in the treatment of symptoms with pharmaceutical preparations.

Many medical doctors have realized the detrimental game into which the pharmaceutical industry has drawn them, and are educating themselves in the field of health, shifting their practices into health-enhancement treatments instead of toxic treatments. This is commendable and should be honored, especially considering the difficulties and peer pressure they endure when their practices no longer revolve around drugs.

As you follow the principles for creating a higher level of health, you will need some assistance to get from where you are to where you want to be. If you are currently on any form of medication, a medical doctor is the best person to assist you in the transition away from drugs. If you are taking any drug at all, it is obvious that, at some level, your body is incapable of restoring health on its own. As you learn and apply the principles I'm sharing with you, in time your body will become capable of restoring your lost health and the drugs will no longer be needed. You will want professional assistance to safely come off the drugs, since most drugs are designed to keep your body addicted to them.

Should a person ever take drugs? Drugs are designed to cause an exact chemical reaction in the body. They are designed as a **crisis remedy** to work almost immediately, thereby possessing the ability to save a person's life at a crisis point.

The wisdom we gain from life's tough lessons lifts us and moves us farther from drama and the crises that expose human ignorance and apathy.

Drugs do not create health. Most people who observe the use of drugs in their own lives come to realize that the long-term use of drugs is like continually placing bandages over a wound that never really heals.

All doctors, regardless of their training, have the moral ability to observe the fruits of their labors and to know if they are providing an enhancement to the lives they touch or merely generating a great business while endangering the lives of their "patients."

So, with the universal scale, "By their fruits you shall know them," you can observe the labors of your doctor and know whether he or she is part of your health problem, or part of the solution.

So, with the universal scale,
"by their fruits you shall know them,"
you can observe the labors of your
doctor and know whether he or she
is part of your health problem,
or part of the solution.

CHAPTER 15

A World Of Cause And Effect

The principle of cause and effect plays a key role in our lives. Because of this truth, I felt that it was appropriate to provide a place to properly honor this powerful principle.

We talked before of the eternal stability of principles. After spending time thinking about it, I find it so comforting to know that we can always trust in the consistency of the principles that regulate our lives on this planet.

When we observe an effect in any area of our lives, we realize that our experience has taught us well what a waste of time it is to deal *only* with the effect. Until we discover and correct the *cause*, the effect will either remain or manifest itself again.

A great example of this principle is if the blender in your kitchen stops working. If you totally ignored the principle of cause and effect, you would acknowledge that the blender had stopped working, and proceed to repair or replace it.

Since we are all aware of this principle in our lives, we realize there are several possible causes that should be considered before we determine the blender is broken. First, you turn the knobs and push the buttons to be sure the settings allow it to operate, then check the cord to be sure it hasn't gotten unplugged, and, finally, check to make sure that electricity is actually being delivered to the outlet.

The only area of our lives where we seem to ignore this principle is with the care of the human body. When a symptom develops, which is the effect of specific causal factors, a treatment is generally prescribed to provide temporary relief from that symptom. Without the training and understanding of the causal levels behind the development of your symptom, your doctor will probably offer a suggested treatment in place of a discussion about the reasons for your symptom. And, when the symptom returns, it will be treated again.

A great example of ignoring this principle is found in the popular treatment for cancer. A malignant tumor is the end resulting effect of many levels of cause. When the tumor is removed and all possible cancer cells surrounding the tumor are either radiated or poisoned with chemotherapy, this is referred to as a proper treatment for cancer. The only problem is that all levels of cause for the development of cancer are still in place and ready to create another tumor in the next weakened area of the body.

In a world of cause and effect, when our choices undermine the health of the body, we suffer the consequences. If our wise choices sustain the body's ability to maintain the balance of health, we get to enjoy that benefit.

Because we live in a world of cause and effect, it becomes the responsibility and opportunity of every individual to learn how the human body functions and how to support it in a way that brings about the restoration and maintenance of true health.

Because we live in a world of cause and effect, it becomes the responsibility and opportunity of every individual to learn how the human body functions and how to support it in a way that brings about the restoration and maintenance of true health.

CHAPTER 16

The Body Is Always Speaking, Is Anyone Listening?

When we are born, we retain the memory of who we are as the essence of life for a short while. Then, in time, our remembrance fades and we are left believing, as does everyone around us, that we are the little bodies running around the house making noise.

The human body was created to guarantee sufficient intelligence to keep it alive and well in two ways. First, there is the design of an ever-evolving cellular wisdom that has the capacity to adapt itself to almost any gradual change in its environment. This cellular wisdom is programmed to be self-healing and capable of perpetually and perfectly reproducing body cells after their kind.

The second way our Creator assured the well-being of the human body was by placing a spark of the Creator's essence into each body.

Such radiant brilliance, permeating the entire human body, is what has caused scientists to universally regard the human body as the absolute epitome of design perfection.

The cellular wisdom keeps a constant 24-hour-a-day vigil doing everything in its power to maintain the homeostatic balance of health. At this level of absolute brilliance, there are so many millions of chemistry functions happening so rapidly throughout the body that a team of scientists couldn't even monitor and identify them as they were happening, let alone duplicate them.

Considering our own part in this performance, all a person needs to do to fulfill his part in this miracle, is listen to the body for his cues and respond intelligently.

Here is the dilemma we must be mature and insightful enough to acknowledge. In the face of such cellular brilliance, *we* keep botching our parts and undermining this cellular intelligence.

As our bodies call for nutrients, we need to consider the foodless garbage we make them dig through just to find a vitamin or a few minerals or anything of nutritional value. Then consider the huge amounts of energy our bodies have to waste sorting and processing, just to end up with something of little value.

Our bodies call for water to wash the stagnated waste from the cells. We get confused and drink soda pop, coffee, alcohol or some other dehydrating substance. These substances not only prevent the body from flushing itself, but also compound the problem through dehydration. Then we wonder why the body won't perform the way we want it to.

The body cries out for sleep, but we think we need to stay up a little longer to finish a project, then maybe just watch a television show that catches our eye, or read a book for a while. As our energy reserves become depleted over the years, we unwittingly wonder what mysterious condition is responsible for the body becoming so fatigued.

It is true that we always maintain our right to reproduce our destructive expectations of life by abusing our bodies. Yet, our intuitive promptings continue to remind us what we really need to do to avoid the painful consequences. Unfortunately, we continue to ignore these reminders.

Confucius once stated: "A man who stumbles over a stone is unwise; a man who stumbles over the same stone twice is a fool." If Confucius coached us on how we continually ignore our many intuitive promptings, I wonder what wisdom he might use to help us really "get it."

Our only hope is to have the sense of humor to laugh at our past foolishness, listen more closely to our inner guidance systems, and cooperate more wisely.

Such radiant brilliance,
permeating the entire human body,
is what has caused scientists to
universally regard the human
body as the absolute epitome
of design perfection.

CHAPTER 17

The Substance Of Which
Degenerative Disease Is Made

Although we have reviewed the two causes of degenerative disease and the nine influences that compound the causes for developing all forms of degenerative disease, I would like to now present the actual substance that is found blocking and clogging every vital pathway, the actual substance that directly causes degenerative disease to exist.

As previously discussed, the real starting point for degenerative disease is in an area that has become weakened due to nerve flow restriction from the brain and spinal column. The nerve flow restriction could be either a primary influence caused by an accident, or it could be a secondary result of stress being held in an area over a long period of time. Either way, the nerve flow restriction is the direct reason for the more permanent condition of weakness in the affected area.

When any area within the body has been weakened, it becomes incapable of clearing itself of the accumulating toxic debris. Not only do the fatigue acids from normal cellular function stagnate in the tissues, but other waste matter the liver is incapable of filtering from the blood begins to naturally deposit itself into the areas that have become too weak to remove it.

When we think of blood, we generally take for granted that our blood is comprised of red blood cells and white blood cells suspended in a sterile fluid. Well, that is correct, but it is not the whole story.

It would be great if our simple perception regarding the content of our blood was accurate, but it isn't. Think for a second how you feel when you have the flu. The discomfort is throughout your body, not because of billions of microorganisms beating you up, but because the virus activated your body's self-cleansing system. This self-cleansing system is the body's brilliant way of detoxifying itself in preparation for healing and restoring body chemistry balance. This process includes the release of toxic debris from tissue storage into the blood as well as the dumping of poisons from the liver into the intestinal tract, a portion of which, unfortunately, also recycles back into the bloodstream.

If you took a sample of your blood at the time you had the flu and looked at it under a microscope, magnified a thousand times, you would be surprised to see all the debris that was making you feel so uncomfortable. You would at least be able to see the metals and chemical crystals, and particles of unusable food residue. These items, along with the acids and other unseen toxic materials, comprise the substances of which degenerative disease is made.

The greatest volume of this material consists of the unusable food waste that results from consuming cooked food and processed foodless foods, not to mention the residue from our meals that stagnates in the intestinal tract and recycles into the bloodstream. Keep in mind that this recycling of the waste from the colon is **the number one reason for fatigue and the main cause for the breakdown of the immune system**. In fact, now that you understand the whole-body influence of the colon, it should make more sense why a person feels "crappy" all over when the colon isn't working well. Then, of course, there are the many chemicals and metals we are exposed to from our food, water and air, and the acid byproducts of normal cellular function as well as the dead tissue cells themselves. And, finally, there is an accumulation of waste materials produced by intestinal parasites and unfriendly bacteria that incubate in the intestinal tract.

On their own, these substances make up a large volume of material that becomes stagnant within the tissues of the body.

This problem is compounded by the years of drinking soft drinks, coffee, alcohol, and milk products instead of water.

Remember all the destructive results of dehydration we reviewed in Chapter 10? All these results strongly compound the stagnation that normally takes place when the body becomes incapable of removing the substances listed above. With the realization that our bodies are comprised of about 70% water, and that the water in the body is stagnant from a lifetime concentration of poison, another large piece of the puzzle falls into place.

And to think we once wondered what mysterious force was causing the body to age and break down. **Knowing the truth might not seem like a great consolation, but that's the beauty and power of knowledge—it removes the limitations of ignorance while opening up a broader selection of beneficial choices.**

That's the beauty and power of knowledge—it removes the limitations of ignorance while opening up a broader selection of beneficial choices.

CHAPTER 18

We Are Each The Product Of Our Own Exposures Of Choice

As we navigate our way through the endless choices that are presented along the path of life, do we ever stop and consider the measurable influence each choice has on our lives?

Only when an obviously destructive result suddenly appears in direct response to a wrong choice do we readily admit to ourselves the association between our choices and the things that keep happening to us.

We are all guilty of maintaining the results of previous wrong choices in various areas of our lives. Until they are seen, recognized for what they are, and eliminated, these destructive obstacles will continue chipping away at the quality of our lives.

I'm referring now to "the stressors in our lives," old residues from past choices that we allow to remain in our lives, beating us up. The reason we allow these little "ankle biters" to remain is because we feel we deserve the punishment they provide since, after all, we made the choice for them to be in our lives!

Before discussing solutions for this long-term issue, I'd like to present an example of how accumulative these destructive stressors can be.

Imagine a person who earns a living coloring cloth in a dye factory. Picture a huge warehouse full of large vats of every imaginable color of dye. Also, picture this person wearing the same set of white cotton clothes every day.

Throughout the day, as the worker handles the various colors, a little red gets splashed onto his white outfit, and later a little splash of green, then blue. By the end of the day, the white cotton clothes demonstrate the influence of every color the worker encountered throughout the day. The cotton clothes might be washed at the end of the day, but the stains remain.

If we looked at this person's white cotton clothes after a year, we might be able to tell by areas in the back that they are white cotton clothes. However, when viewed from the front, the influence of the dyes would be so great that it would prevent anyone from recognizing that the person had been wearing white clothes.

A few years of holding onto unnecessary stressors might just show a few "splashes" of deterioration in the quality of life but, in time, **the accumulative effects of stress will destroy a person's quality of life.**

Wouldn't it be great if every one of our choices in life were the perfect long-term choice? Of course, this would be the ultimate accomplishment for a human on earth.

Making incorrect choices is just a part of the human experience. Incorrect choices bring with them negative consequences from which we can choose to learn. When we learn the lessons that accompany our wrong choices, we become more capable of making wiser choices in the future.

Albert Einstein and Thomas Edison were two wise and successful men who knew very well the necessity of learning from their mistakes. As Albert Einstein stated: "Anyone who has never made a mistake has never tried anything new." Thomas Edison was no stranger to trial and error as he admitted: "I have not failed. I've just found 10,000 ways that won't work."

So here we are today, surrounded by the results of the thousands of choices we made in the past. Some of those were good choices and some were not. The individuals, things and circumstances that make up our lives are the accumulated sum total of our many personal choices. The great news is, just as we have the right to drop destructive beliefs from our personal belief systems, we have every right to remove every destructive stressor from our lives!

What is it in your life that is out of harmony with the fulfillment of your heart's desires?

If you were to list every stressor in your life, you would see that each one represents a wrong choice from the past that, at present, doesn't serve you in a productive or harmonious manner.

Below is a four-step exercise for healing and clearing your life of all stressors. This exercise is entitled, very simply:

The Four-Step Stressor Clearing Exercise

1) Begin by listing every stressor you currently have in your life.
2) Then, one at a time, ask yourself why you have chosen to include this issue as part of your life, and record your answer.
3) Next, ask yourself what lessons you have learned from each specific issue.
4) When you have finished the lesson, since you are free to release the stressor from your life, set a goal for the time frame in which you plan to permanently eliminate each stressor, then work toward the fulfillment of that goal.

What would it feel like to work with this technique until you were living a totally stress-free life? Remember, it is only false beliefs that hold our stressors in our lives. Therefore, when we truly learn the lesson each stressor represents, there is no reason for it to remain.

As we are busy erasing the whiteboard of our past wrong choices, we must also ask how we can wisely make better choices today and avoid replacing the old stressors with new ones. All it takes is a minute to pause and review the above exercise, then ask ourselves whether this is another automatic, emotional choice, or a wise and beneficial decision.

It only makes sense that, if a person takes the time to complete the exercise above, as well as the necessary minute to pause and evaluate each new choice, there is no more reason for living a stressful life.

Just as we have the right to
drop destructive beliefs from our
personal belief systems, we have
every right to remove every
destructive stressor from
our lives!

CHAPTER 19

Recipe For Disease

By now I hope it is clear that the development of degenerative disease is quite predictable and without mystery, other than the man-made mysteries. The greatest element that interrupts the predictability of developing degenerative disease is **a self-destructive individual with a strong and powerful mental override**. While any form of self-destruction is always a clear sign of emotional damage that must be healed, a strong, healthy mental outlook has the power to override a great deal of the self-destructive effects.

If a powerfully positive mental outlook can assist a normally self-destructive individual in avoiding the consequences of a destructive lifestyle, then consider how health-enhancing such an attitude could be for an individual who is willing to heal and correct all levels of cause behind disease and create a high level of true health!

Just in case there is still any confusion regarding the consistent and predictable breakdown of the abused human body, I would like to produce a few examples of how specific degenerative diseases develop.

To make this simple, let's pretend we're in a bakery and every disease is a different kind of cake we're going to make.

Each of our cakes begins with the same basic ingredients: flour, milk, eggs, butter, and sugar. From this foundation, we will vary the amounts of the base ingredients and add other ingredients and flavorings. In the end, we will have dozens of distinctively different cakes.

In the same manner, every disease begins with the same fundamental ingredients.

In order to establish our basic recipe, from which a variety of degenerative diseases are created, begin by placing

the following ingredients into an innocent, impressionable human child:

- Start with the DNA memory of thousands of traumatic experiences to activate fear and contractiveness within the tissues of the child's body.
- Add to this many personal traumatic memories and perceived traumatic memories.
- Add one misalignment of the upper vertebrae of the neck. This is used to reduce the communication from the brain to specific areas of the body, thereby causing weaknesses in these areas.
- Add plenty of white sugar, cooked foods, processed grains, dairy products and processed foods (especially in the form of treats, desserts and fast food snacks).
- Be sure to provide information regarding tragedies that are currently happening all around us, confirming the constant threat of earthly life and establishing a very limiting and inhibited expectation of life.

Now, from such a simple basic recipe, we can take an adult body in many directions, producing an unlimited number of diseases. To make sure our results are consistently similar, it is best to always begin with the basic recipe outlined above.

Let's begin with a very popular, but basic, condition: chronic fatigue syndrome. To our basic recipe, we need to add lots of antibiotics. It doesn't matter whether the source is a medical doctor or the dairy and poultry industries. The antibiotics, along with chlorinated water, make certain that the friendly intestinal flora is destroyed, allowing for an overgrowth of unfriendly bacteria. Without the friendly bacteria to neutralize the toxic waste generated by the overgrowth of the unfriendly bacteria, the colon is turned into a toxic septic system. **The recycling of this poison from the colon into the lymph and blood is the number one reason for fatigue and the breakdown of the immune system.**

Next, it helps if the person is a workaholic. In this way, as the fatigue acids and poisons from the colon cycle into the blood-stream, the demand for more energy will justify the use of willpower, coffee or sugar (or all three), which drives the adrenal glands into exhaustion. In time, the bloodstream becomes absolutely saturated with fatigue acids and the adrenal glands are exhausted. Add to this some other less significant conditions such as a stress-induced slow metabolism, hormone imbalances, and the results of exhaustion of other glands. The sum total of these patterns leaves a person absolutely poisoned and exhausted: hence, **chronic fatigue syndrome**.

The reason chronic fatigue syndrome is so closely associated with fibromyalgia is because CFS is the ideal base for the development of fibromyalgia. With all the conditions of CFS in place, the liver is incapable of keeping the blood clean enough, so the lymphatic system becomes stagnated, which forces the **Substance Of Which Degenerative Disease is Made** into the muscle tissue. This causes direct stress to the tissue cells. In any area of the body where the cells become stressed, the body provides its choice of a pain-reducing solution, which happens to be calcium. Calcium neutralizes the acidic fluids and sedates tissue pain. The problem with this natural sedation process is that an accumulation of calcium and phosphates develops among the tissue cells. In time, both minerals begin to crystallize. When the calcium and phosphates crystallize, it's like having sand crystals that constantly grind into a person's muscle tissue. These sand crystals are irritating and damaging to the cells, causing an even greater amount of inflammation and pain than that which was originally caused by the acid waste in the same areas. This is the reason **fibromyalgia is "medically incurable."** It is impossible to reverse a toxic condition with toxic drugs. Yet, by understanding how and why the condition has developed, an individual is free to make lifestyle changes that will correct the causes and dissolve the sand. As the sand is removed from tissue storage, the pain is eliminated and the individual is able to return to a comfortable way of life.

Systemic cancer (such as breast cancer, prostate cancer, lymphoma, etc.) is another very common, predictable, and totally preventable condition for which we can create a recipe.

We begin again with the same basic recipe. For this condition, we need an extra-strong ingredient. We need one bunch of suppressed hate, anger or resentment. We can usually find this in a "nice" person, because nice people often solicit love and acceptance to soothe the pain they hold within.

Chinese medicine teaches that the emotions of hate, anger and resentment are held in the liver. This creates a contractiveness that undermines the function of the liver, and in time allows for an excess accumulation of cholesterol plaque and other toxic waste. The liver then becomes overwhelmed with waste materials filtered from the blood, and its ability to clean the blood is diminished. When the brain registers that the liver is no longer able to keep the blood sufficiently clean, it is forced to find other ways of cleaning the blood. The brain's first emergency solution is to tighten the muscles under the collarbones, the area where the lymphatic fluids from the body flow into the bloodstream. This is done to hold the lymphatic waste out of the blood, allowing the liver to catch up on its workload. When this lymphatic stagnation occurs, it becomes the starting point of tissue poisoning and the development of the substance called cellulite, which is stagnated lymph, not fat cells.

At this point, anyone considering what we have covered so far can already see the entire foundation for breast cancer. If you were to check a thousand women with breast cancer, you would find a thousand women with the exact causal condition described above, very well established.

In fact, for a woman who has this exact causal condition firmly established and does *not* have cancer, it is only a matter of time until the stagnation of lymphatic waste accumulates in the breast, stressing the tissue and thereby causing a similar calcium buffer to that experienced with fibromyalgia. Calcification of the breast tissue always takes place after the tissue has been stressed for years due to lymphatic stagnation.

It is very common to hear the expression, "early detection of breast cancer." This is a term used for promoting the use of mammograms for the detection of breast tumors. The problem is, when a woman has a build-up of lymphatic waste in her breast tissue, (as a high percentage of women do) it's just a matter of time until the tissue develops a calcification problem. When you crush calcium crystals into tissue cells that are already starved for blood flow and oxygen due to lymphatic stagnation, the damaged tissue will quickly become inflamed. Then, since radiation is the number one activator of mutation, to radiate (x-ray) the inflamed, oxygen-starved tissue cells of the breast is the most ideal way to activate the mutation process and, **thereby, cause breast cancer**.

In place of "early detection of breast cancer," a more factual statement would be: "early *creation* of breast cancer."

It is actually very difficult to create cancer. It generally takes many years of consistent suppression of emotions. We must ignore our intuitive warnings *and* our physical warnings; and we must collect large volumes of the Substance Of Which Degenerative Disease Is Made. This is accomplished by using over-the-counter drugs to suppress colds, flu, and other symptoms. We have been led to believe that our symptoms are bad and must be treated and eliminated. In reality, however, colds and flu are two of the body's brilliant efforts to clean house so that the balance of health can be restored. But, since our preference is to not be inconvenienced by such "house cleanings," we generally suppress the reactions as quickly as possible, which holds the waste within the body and blocks the pathways where life is meant to flow.

As difficult as it is to create cancer, every year there are at least 1.2 million self-destructive individuals in the United States who do just that. Present U.S. statistics show that 1.2 million people are diagnosed with cancer **every year**.

The three most direct and immediate reasons for tissue cells to mutate into cancer cells are:

1) Tissue cells are starved for oxygen because of poor blood circulation in the immediate area.

2) Trapped blood proteins, and the Substance Of Which Degenerative Disease Is Made, stagnate in a weakened area due to an overwhelmed liver that is unable to keep the blood clean. This condition causes stagnation and a back pressure within the lymphatic system.

3) Nerve flow restriction that makes the affected area too weak to properly detoxify itself.

From the patterns we have already observed, it should be obvious how a person could whip up a bit of **arthritis**.

As with cancer, arthritis requires an extra-strong emotional component as the active ingredient. **Resentment** usually works best as an activator of arthritis. When a generous helping of resentment is added to the basic recipe, the distinct core blend for the condition results. Next, you need the misaligned neck to either directly reduce the nerve flow to the hands or to transfer tension to the lower back, reducing nerve flow and weakening the lower extremities. In most cases, both are happening, stagnating the colon, overwhelming the liver and loading the weakened area with toxic materials. It is just a matter of time before the stressed and weakened tissues are sedated with calcium, and the calcium crystallizes, causing inflammation of the joints. Arthritis is the common term used to identify a condition of inflamed joints.

In fact, all calcification problems—such as arthritis, bone spurs, calcified breast tissue, and fused joints or vertebrae—are the result of the same process. An area becomes weakened, stressed, and then sedated with calcium. Then the calcium crystallizes, which sets up a secondary inflammatory condition.

Three very destructive effects intensify every type of degenerative disease. In fact, these three effects are always present and always cause most of the destruction in every type of degenerative disease.

First, because a large volume of toxic waste stagnates within the lymphatic system when a degenerative disease is present, this poison saturates the tissue cells, weakening them and greatly increasing direct tissue destruction. As the tissue cell destruction gets out of control, huge volumes of uric acid are released, which cause gout and many other inflammatory conditions. The increased tissue destruction also releases and activates enormous numbers of free radicals. When a liver is overwhelmed and becomes incapable of producing sufficient antioxidants to hold these free radicals in check, they begin to multiply exponentially, out of control. **The level of free radicals throughout the body is the only true scale for measuring the overall degeneration of any disease.** The third effect that compounds the destruction of every degenerative disease is the presence of parasites and unfriendly microorganisms.

Every organic farmer knows that, if the soil contains the necessary minerals, the vitality of the crop will remain high enough to repel pests, making pesticides unnecessary. If the soil is weakened, or the minerals are out of balance, the plants grow weak and immediately attract the pests that will destroy them and assist them in returning to the soil.

The same principle applies to the human body. As long as all vital conditions allow the energy of the body to remain high, parasites and unfriendly microorganisms are held in check. However, as soon as the energy drops to a consistently low level, parasites and organisms begin their out-of-control reproduction. The lower the energy levels, the more prolific the parasitic life forms become.

So, you see, there is logic at every level of the development of degenerative disease. If we simply compare the human body to the world around us, we suddenly grasp a simpler understanding of the once-mysterious body.

That's the sad part of the health/disease dilemma with which America has been faced for the past hundred years. Much of the information I'm presenting has been purposely and force-fully suppressed. Greed has demanded that an understanding of these principles be suppressed, while human fear and suffering continues to be exchanged for money.

Because of this suppression of information, there has never been the funding or the motivation to research the principles of health. The other problem is that we have all been looking for relief from suffering, rather than for an understanding of the levels of cause that lead to the development of human diseases.

It doesn't really matter why this information hasn't been available before. All that *does* matter is what you do with it now that you have it.

What I am presenting in this book will never be validated by medical science. There will never be double blind studies performed on these systems and techniques. The obvious reason it will never happen is because research funding will always be directed toward treatments that will only bring temporary relief to the sufferer while inhibiting the body from healing itself. If everyone were to follow the principles I teach, and if everyone lost his or her fear of the great mysteries of disease, "The Great Oz" would be exposed. And, in the absence of the fear that is generated by the threat of disease, how many of us would continue dumping buckets of money into the bottomless pit of medical research?

Every person who diligently follows the principles I am presenting will also become fully aware of the fact that a perfectly healthy person doesn't require any form of treatment!

Every person who diligently follows the principles I am presenting will also become fully aware of the fact that a perfectly healthy person doesn't require any form of treatment!

CHAPTER 20

The Long And Winding Road
Of A Hands-On Researcher

I've discovered that there are two major types of researchers in the world. There is the hands-on researcher who studies everything he can find regarding a chosen subject and then, very patiently, spends years testing and observing, contemplating and evaluating. Throughout the years of my own research, I have gained a great deal of respect for the true hands-on researchers of our world. Such a researcher may spend twenty years making only four or five breakthrough observations, but these are the observations that clarify and simplify the fundamental structures of life and therefore possess the power to move the world forward and away from the status quo.

The second type of researcher is a reporter, who, without a feel for the personal testing and proof that led the hands-on researchers to their conclusions, will present his own opinions on the subject, formulated from the life experiences he possessed before studying the subject on which he is reporting.

For ten years of my adult life, I was an enthusiastic student of the world of natural health and therapies. Then, during my time as director of a holistic cancer clinic, my life shifted, and I fully engaged in what became a twenty-year intensive hands-on research project.

I had to make certain observations hundreds, and sometimes thousands of times just to prepare myself to see the simplicity of what I needed to see. Now I would like to tell you the stories of when I "saw" the key principles that have allowed me to understand the simple side of health and disease.

During the two years I directed the cancer clinic, I worked alongside our medical director evaluating patient chemistries and designing individual treatment schedules. After observing hundreds of similar blood studies and chemistry patterns, I realized that every person with cancer or any other serious degenerative disease had the same body chemistry profile as the next person diagnosed with a serious degenerative condition.

By that time, all I wanted to do was go "upstream" from the position of degenerative disease, and gain a greater understanding of the levels of cause that were responsible for the resulting patterns that looked so common among all cancer patients.

Before I left the clinic, I formulated three consistent observations:

1) Every person with a degenerative disease has been poisoned for years due to a liver that is overwhelmed and incapable of cleaning the bloodstream.

2) Every person with a degenerative disease has an excessive amount of free radical destruction throughout the entire body that is out of control.

3) The proper digestion of food has been impaired for so long that the body has been seriously starved for essential nutrients and poisoned by undigested food residues.

So, I went out into the world just wanting to know the answer to one simple question: **Why?**

At every stage of my research, I continued asking the question: **Why?** I eventually discovered that when you sincerely want to know the answer to that question, it will be found at deeper levels than you ever imagined, and will come from the most surprising and simple sources.

The first story I will share with you took place in Providence, Rhode Island, about eighteen years ago.

I was performing health screens for the second or third time on a group to whom I had been teaching the principles of health. Realizing that everyone was deficient in both enzymes and nutrients, I suggested that each person heavily boost their enzyme levels by using enzyme-enhanced vitamins and minerals as well as before-meal digestive enzymes.

When I returned to Providence six weeks later, I was surprised to find that every person's health screen showed patterns indicative of a liver that was overwhelmed. Every health screen also revealed patterns indicating the reproductive areas of their bodies had become congested.

After three days of health screens, I realized that somehow the intense enzyme program was responsible for the patterns I was seeing. I adjusted everyone's program and advised three ginger baths per week for the next six weeks. When I returned six weeks later, all liver and reproductive patterns had been cleared.

From this observation, along with a few thousand additional health screens, I realized something that is now so simple to explain. **Whenever you increase the vitality of the body, its natural response is to release toxic materials from tissue storage in preparation for normalizing the health of the body**. Colds and flu are the natural techniques the body uses to prepare itself for healing and normalizing chemistry functions. In a toxic state of overwhelm and reduced vitality the body isn't able to properly heal itself or restore its natural functions. To counteract this, it shifts into a cleansing mode such as a cold or the flu. At the same time, the body loudly signals to us to reduce our activities and food intake until enough accumulated waste has been removed to allow the body to restore its energy reserves and heal itself.

Before my discovery of the way the body uses both the male and female reproductive areas to handle the liver's overload, I coached men and women in the same ineffective way the rest of the world did. I would advise them as though the cause of the problem was within the reproductive system itself. From my observations in Providence, along with another discovery I will share with you, I have been able to teach dozens of men (including my older brother) how to support their bodies to reverse prostate cancer, mostly by clearing the liver and gallbladder and opening up the nerve flow from the lower back. Those are the two most direct and immediate causes for the development of prostate cancer.

The next story I would like to tell you was the absolute key to my discovering the secret for reversing chronic fatigue syndrome.

On my way to Providence every six weeks, I made a couple of stops. One of these stops was in Iowa. On the last evening of one of my Iowa stays, I was screening a mother of eight children. She had told me of her chronic fatigue and constant brain fog, along with many other related symptoms. In fact, she claimed, "it's a darn good thing I have so many kids always calling me mamma, or I'd forget who the heck I am."

After seeing that her blood looked more like sewer water than blood, I asked if she would mind if I worked on her lower back for a few minutes as an experiment. She readily agreed, as she admitted having a lot of tension and pain in that area. I spent about fifteen minutes pressing and kneading the muscles of her lower back with the heel of my hand. When I finished, she sat in her chair for a few seconds, then jumped up and said, "I'm sorry, I have to use the restroom," and quickly walked out of the room. In about five minutes, she came back in and sat down again. She couldn't hide her amazement any more than she could hide her embarrassment as she blurted out, "my gosh, I've never seen such a bowel movement as the one I just had, it filled the whole toilet bowl!"

Her experience was an exciting confirmation of a theory I had been working on for months. I congratulated her and assured her that if she took a detox bath that evening, drank plenty of water and went to bed early that she would feel surprisingly better the next morning. She did as I suggested and phoned me the next week to confirm that her experience was exactly as I had predicted.

I immediately phoned the husband of a woman in Palm Springs, California, with whom I had been working for several weeks. I excitedly informed him that I knew for sure how to coach him to help his wife. I explained a few techniques for him to use on her back and advised other additional steps to add to her program. Within weeks, his wife (whom he had been literally *carrying* in for her appointments with me) began coming back to life. A few months later Dr. Bruce Russell, a chiropractor with a large practice in Victoria, British Columbia, asked me to come to Victoria and work with a group of his patients who had similar problems.

Because the Palm Springs woman was from Victoria, she and her husband traveled to Victoria three or four times a year to visit her family. During each visit, her husband would literally deposit her body onto the therapy table, Dr. Russell would make the necessary adjustments, and her husband would carry her out again.

A few months later, the president of a chronic fatigue support group in Victoria called me and explained that Dr. Russell gave her my phone number and assured her that I could help her and her group.

Within weeks, I made my first visit to Victoria and presented my work to about fifty people with chronic fatigue syndrome. Over the next few days, I performed health screens on as many people as I was able to during that first visit. Then, just before I left Victoria, I stopped by to meet Dr. Russell. It was during this visit that he explained how he had known and worked with the woman from Palm Springs for years. For months, she had appeared more corpse-like than alive. Suddenly, this same woman blew into his office like an electron bouncing off the walls, and claimed that the difference in her life was what I had been teaching her and her husband.

I continued working with the group and, after a few months, ninety percent of them began feeling so much better that they discontinued attending the support group. Instead, they began meeting together at the home of the support group's president with a completely opposite focus. Rather than helping each other find ways to live with their conditions, **they were all supporting one another in the journey back into life**.

As I mentioned before, it was about eighteen years ago that I worked with that group. Rebecca Clarkson was one of the original members of that group in Victoria. When I met Rebecca, she was doing her best to fit her whole real estate business, as well as her entire personal life, into the three-hour window during which she was able to get out of bed each day. Rebecca not only had chronic fatigue syndrome, but fibromyalgia and several other very uncomfortable complications as well. Today, she is one of the main health coaches in my office.

Rebecca is a coach whom I would refer to as a true authority on health. Rebecca reversed many of the most difficult conditions a person can suffer from. She reversed the pain, the exhaustion, the emotional depression and all levels of cause that had taken a lifetime to develop. Rebecca can honestly say, "I've been there, and I've reversed it all." As a health coach, Rebecca can relate to most anyone and always offers a compassionate helping hand. Rebecca remains a glowing example of true health.

Another stopping point on my tour of the U.S. was a chiropractic office in Bakersfield. The doctor in this office was a naturopathic doctor as well as a chiropractor. Every six weeks he would gather his patients together, and I would present a lesson to them. For a couple of days thereafter, I would perform health screens on these patients. This doctor's focus was very much on treating his patient's symptoms with herbs. He requested that I simply perform the health screens, write reports for each patient and provide him with my results. From the insights he gained from my evaluations, he treated their symptoms accordingly.

Each time I visited his office and screened the same people, I kept a log of their results. After my fourth visit, I studied everyone's results very closely and suddenly began to see consistent patterns. When the patient showed a toxic blood pattern, the doctor's treatment would be to clean the blood. The next time I would find a toxic liver and lymphatic pattern. The following visit would show the transfer of the stress point to another specific area of the body. As I put it all together I realized very clearly that **targeted treatment of symptoms only transfers the *Substance Of Which Degenerative Disease is Made* from one area of the body to another, thereby transferring the *symptoms* from one area to another**. For the first time in my life, I understood the power of supporting the body to maintain a continuous flow of this waste material through specific channels, and clearing it completely. It wasn't long after this experience that I discovered the most vital key for total detoxification. I refer to this vital key as: ***The Flow Of Detoxification.* Until a person really understands The Flow Of Detoxification, it isn't possible to totally detoxify the body.**

Before I conclude this chapter, I will tell you one more story about a person I coached about a dozen years ago. He was probably the first person with prostate cancer I had coached to create a higher level of health with The Body Chemistry Support System.

I had known this man for several years before he came into my office for this particular health screen. He was a person who normally always joked around, but on this day he had a very sober attitude. He told me that he had just been diagnosed with prostate cancer and wanted me to confirm this with a health screening. After confirming that all the causal patterns for his diagnosis were definitely present, I offered him a challenge. I said, "why don't you just reverse all these reasons for your prostate developing the problems, and trust that your body can rid itself of the cancer?" So that he wouldn't feel as though he had to carry on forever to accomplish such a project, I outlined an intense health program and challenged him to complete it within four months.

After four months, he returned to his doctor for a check-up and to repeat the PSA test. While he was waiting for his test results, he decided he just didn't want to hang around the doctor's office any longer. He announced to the nurse that he didn't really need his report after all because he was fine and that he was going home now. One of the receptionists was shocked with his statement and, with a very authoritarian attitude, stated, "how can you say that you're fine, you don't even have your test results back." My friend spun around, leaned over the reception counter and, with absolute confidence, said, **"I *do* know, because I did the work!"**

I consider it a real privilege to be involved in the work that I do. There can't be many occupations in the world more satisfying than coaching people to support their bodies in restoring the life essence that allows true joy and health to return. **The amazing and fun thing is this: it works every time the program is followed.**

It becomes possible to
totally detoxify the body,
only when a person really
understands the flow
of detoxification.

CHAPTER 21

Reversing The Causes Of Aging And Disease

Now that you know exactly how we got up the proverbial creek without the proverbial paddle, I'm sure you'll agree that it would be a great idea to find the map that leads back to safety.

We have covered in detail the causes, the influences, and the effects that are collectively responsible for the breakdown of health, and the reasons for aging and disease.

The major difference between what I teach and the information generally available in the health field is this: **when you clearly understand cause, then correct it, the body will handle the details for reversing and clearing the effects.**

Why would a person ever want to do the necessary work to reverse the causes of aging and disease? After all, it goes against the flow of everything we've been doing all our lives.

It's interesting to see how many people are actually discovering that what they have been doing for the past few decades just hasn't worked. A few other issues have motivated people to cultivate the willingness to do whatever it takes to change their lives for the better. A few of these motivators are:

- People are finally getting tired of continuously trying to eliminate *symptoms*, only to be told that they need to "learn to live with them."
- People are getting in touch with the harsh reality that, within a relatively short period of time, a person could wake up and find he or she has become lonely and old, in diapers, with a broken-down body, incapable of any kind of meaningful self-care.
- People may be finding themselves suffering and waiting to die from painful degenerative diseases.

- **Or, better yet, someone might have inspired them with the knowledge of how to reverse the reasons for aging and disease and create true health, thereby allowing them to enjoy a very high quality of life to the end**.

To successfully reverse a lifetime accumulation of toxic waste from the body—and the accompanying accumulated damage—certain essential conditions and requirements must be met.

A person must first possess, or generate, a strong enough **desire** to achieve such a goal. That must be followed by a strong enough **commitment** to maintain the motivation to keep going beyond the relief from suffering. **Unfortunately, most people lose their motivation to continue the work once they experience some relief from their pain and discomfort.** Sadly, they will never know the exhilaration of restoring the spark of life back into their bodies.

Since trauma is the primary cause of all disease, it would seem logical to begin by healing trauma. Although ideally true, that approach has its challenges. By the time we become sufficiently inundated by the discomforts and limitations of our self-destruction, we are generally too far out of touch with our traumas to be able to heal them. The body is usually far too saturated with the poisons that dull our awareness, including the awareness that healing our traumas is even a possibility. Then, of course, our long-term expectations of life keep us in a frame of mind that generally isn't open to the necessary shift in perspective.

So, rather than remaining stuck, the answer is to follow a plan that has already proven to bring about the desired success. I will review that a little later.

Every time the body is hurt, or even perceives hurt, the habit of self-protection gets stronger. This is a natural survival technique. Getting hurt is a form of stress to which the body reacts by developing adaptive coping mechanisms. An obvious example of this is the development of calluses on our hands. The first day of digging with a shovel produces blisters. By the third day, the body's defense mechanisms have already created rapid tissue growth that forms a thick layer of leather-like skin to protect the delicate tissue cells beneath the surface of that skin. This is just one of the many ways the body adapts to harsh environments. The average adult body has built up dozens of such adaptations. If these adaptations aren't recognized, the total reversal process will seem a little confusing due to mild reactions and the length of time it takes to reverse some adaptations. At the same time, though, the wisdom of the body can always be trusted. You can also trust that the system I have designed for you **allows your body's wisdom to be in complete control, which, in turn, always creates a miraculous outcome.**

The starting point for reversing the entire lifetime accumulation of toxic waste, tissue destruction, levels of adaptation, and diminished life within the body is through whole-body detoxification.

The toxic debris that saturates the tissue cells of the body and pollutes the bloodstream is the main cause for fatigue and diminished life within the body. So, if we want to restore this life energy, we must begin by **"taking out the trash."**

Your body knows exactly how to detoxify itself on a daily basis. The problem is that we have interfered with this natural process for so many years that the body is no longer capable of successfully accomplishing this task on its own. The heart of the work that every person must do to successfully allow the body to restore its natural functions is presented in the next chapter as **The Body Chemistry Support System**.

It is not my purpose to turn this book into an instruction manual. **My purpose is to identify the problems with which we are all too familiar, then affirm that there is a real solution, so that true hope can motivate you to create a quality of life beyond anything you ever dreamed possible**.

It isn't my intention to excite you about the solutions I'm presenting, only to leave you without practical directions. The backbone of my work is educational. If I am able to assure your success, then all my years of research have been time well spent. The Body Chemistry Support System works *every time* for *every person* who faithfully implements it. The reason for this is that my staff and I do everything we can to make sure our clients understand how to implement the program. We are always developing ways to simplify the instructions and perfect the program. You will find continual updates regarding our instructional and support materials on our website at: **www.drmickhall.com**

As you follow The Body Chemistry Support System, be aware of the necessity of reopening the five pathways of life! There are many ways you can incorporate the help of others to accomplish the required work. We will help guide you to successfully accomplish what is necessary.

Since each of us is the actual author of our present physical condition, it is essential that we personally accept responsibility for the work that must be done to reverse the damage and blockages within our own bodies.

In order to reopen these pathways and accomplish the work that will restore the natural functions to the body, **you** are the one who must be fully responsible, and it is **you** who will need to do the bulk of the work, regardless of any professionals you might hire to assist you.

Most adults in the U.S. are on the verge of total exhaustion. Some who are closer to the edge than others believe they still have plenty of energy because their nervous systems are so hyper, due to the irritating effects of stress and the acid waste bathing their nerve cells. Such a person will claim they have "too much energy." The truth is, it isn't high energy they are experiencing, it's just nervous agitation!

Low energy, and its associated nervous agitation, is one of the main causes of sleep disorders. Once it begins, the problem is compounded by lack of sleep, thereby causing additional fatigue. In such a state of sleep deprivation, the individual doesn't have enough energy to even sleep through the night, which proves that you need true energy in order to relax and remain in a deep sleep.

As you might guess, the greatest solution for most sleep disorders is to remove the irritating waste from the body through effective detoxification. As the body is effectively detoxified, the main cause of fatigue is eliminated, increasing the energy and thereby allowing the individual to finally relax and sleep comfortably all night.

Because of our misconceptions of what a caffeine or sugar high or an adrenaline rush really is, most people confuse those states with what it feels like to have plenty of energy. The truth is, being locked in a room with a bunch of hyperactive children after they consumed a large bag of Halloween candy would be considered an absolute nightmare for most adults. That is exactly what happens to an adult's body after the stimulating and irritating effects of coffee or sugar.

None of these are examples of high energy. They're examples of hyperactivity through agitation. True energy is calming and peaceful. Energy enhances the joys of life and soothes the rough spots.

Before continuing, I would like to ask you to take a moment and consider the most enjoyable experiences of your daily life, even if you just quickly consider only one or two. Now, imagine your enjoyment of those experiences multiplied by four. Do you think you could handle that? It's available to you if you are willing to do the work to allow all your life energy to be restored to your body.

If you really embrace the vision of the last paragraph, I assure you that your efforts will be well rewarded.

Just as a point of reference, I'll list below the issues you need to address in order to detoxify your body, restore the essence of life, and allow for the good of your life to flow uninhibitedly to you.

You need to faithfully follow The Body Chemistry Support System for three years, longer if there is a pre-existing condition, or if consistency is lacking. Your diligent application of this program, along with a healthy exercise program, will allow your body to catch up with its healing and balancing work.

- Spinal misalignments must be corrected.
- The gallbladder must be cleared out repeatedly so the liver can clean itself.
- Dental work must be done correctly; this is much more important for the health of the body than most people realize.
- The traumatic memories responsible for our reduced expectations, and the stressors in our lives, must be healed; this is vital to long term success and happiness.
- Consistent forgiveness must be practiced—forgiveness of everyone and everything that has activated the fear that has been held in your life and body.

With every step of your detoxification, with every spinal adjustment, with every infection you clear, with every density you forgive and release, the essence of life will be allowed to return. **With the complete return of the essence of life will come your greatest peace, joy and satisfaction!**

With the complete return
of the essence of life will
come your greatest peace,
joy and satisfaction!

CHAPTER 22

The Body Chemistry Support System

During my twenty-year research project, every time I discovered a solution to the destructive patterns or problems I was observing, I built that solution into the program I named **The Body Chemistry Support System**.

The true power of this evolving program wasn't that I was providing better ways of fixing the body faster—it was just the opposite. **I discovered that the true power for healing the human body was in learning how to properly support the brilliant self-healing processes that our creator already programmed into the body, not to insult this wisdom by always trying to "fix" it.**

I also discovered issues that prevent the body from keeping up with healing the ongoing damage that is inflicted onto it. They are as follows:

- Our self-destructive expectations cause us to automatically repeat self-sabotaging activities that undermine the body's self-regulating systems.
- Our self-destructive expectations keep drawing stressful circumstances into our lives and prompt us to live and eat in a manner that destroys our vitality and starves the body of necessary nutrients.
- Our self-destructive expectations repeatedly place us in harm's way.

Here is the bottom line: **The brilliantly programmed body knows exactly how to heal itself if we will only *support* it in doing so, rather than *harming* it faster than it can heal!**

The starting point for Body Chemistry Support is the recognition that the innate wisdom of the body is in charge of the entire healing and restoration project. We must honor this wisdom by providing support for what the body needs, rather than imposing our personal agendas onto it.

157

Body Chemistry Support isn't an improvement on past activities that haven't worked. Its focus is exactly the opposite. Body Chemistry Support enhances the body's own superior wisdom in accomplishing the goals of healing and balancing health rather than focusing on what a person doesn't wish to experience, or wishes to treat and eliminate.

Body Chemistry Support is the core of the newest and most effective branch of the healing arts: Human Biorestorology.

When an anatomical picture of the human body is studied, it is clear that at the core of the body is the intestinal tract. A close study of the chemistry functions of the body teaches us that *the content of the entire intestinal tract determines the content of the bloodstream. The content of the bloodstream supplies the materials for the chemistry of the body, and the body chemistry then determines immediate health or disease.*

Therefore, when a person attempts to correct imbalances or apparent distortions within the body without first supporting the intestinal tract to normalize its functions, it's like trying to drive your car with one foot on the gas pedal and the other on the brake—you just don't get very far.

Priority #1—Intestinal Tract Support:

The starting point of every proper health-restoring program **must always be** the intestinal tract. Whatever other work is done before the intestinal tract is properly supported will only be partially beneficial. The powerful influence of the intestinal tract on the bloodstream guarantees that progress will be inhibited until the intestinal work is accomplished.

Three essential issues must be addressed in order to ensure the natural functioning of the intestinal tract. First, **the selection, preparation and digestion of food must be improved**, in order for the necessary nutrients to be delivered into the bloodstream.

The second essential issue is to remove the following three forms of waste from the intestinal tract as rapidly as possible:

- Residue from ingested food.
- Toxic waste filtered from the blood by the liver and released into the intestinal tract by the gallbladder.
- Old accumulated waste that has **stagnated** within the intestinal tract for years due to poor digestion and sluggish elimination.

The third area of support for the intestinal tract is the rebalancing of the intestinal flora that has been destroyed by chlorinated water and antibiotics.

The secret key for building a clean, strong bloodstream is a fully supported intestinal tract. This will begin to boost your vitality and stabilize your strength.

Priority #2—Support For The Cleaning Of The Blood And Lymph:

The next priority of Body Chemistry Support is the cleaning of the blood and lymph directly through the skin. After elimination of waste through the colon, the skin—which is the largest organ of elimination—is the body's second choice for detoxifying itself. As the body perspires, it releases toxic materials from the blood and lymph.

Therefore, the second priority in Body Chemistry Support is to enhance the natural process of elimination by taking a detox bath. A detox bath increases the opening of the pores of the skin and, at the same time, draws much larger volumes of metals and chemicals out through the skin. This allows the body to remove much more waste and greatly reduces the burden placed on the liver to clean waste from the blood.

As you advance your way into Body Chemistry Support, you will realize that it is much like the old circus act where the performer started spinning one plate on top of a long stick. After the first was spinning, he would start another, then another. In a short time, he would have a dozen plates spinning on top of the sticks.

When you begin, you may feel most comfortable just following the first two priorities of Body Chemistry support: intestinal support and the detox baths. This is like practicing with two plates spinning until you are confident enough to add another.

Priority #3—Nutritional Support:

The third priority is **nutritional support**. In the field of natural health, this has generally been considered the highest priority. I would like to encourage you to reverse the old focus of asking, "what should I take to fix my body?" I prefer that you ask, "What needs to be removed from my body to allow it to normalize its own functions?"

The good news is that you don't have to figure out for yourself what your body really needs. I've spent most of my adult life figuring that out for you. That's why the results produced by **The Body Chemistry Support System** have become almost totally predictable. All that is required is that a person accept responsibility for authoring his physical experience in life and make a commitment to do the work necessary to improve the quality of his life. With the help of The Body Chemistry Support System, along with the information we provide, anyone can create a higher level of health than has ever been experienced.

The way Body Chemistry Support is to be interwoven into a complete success program is presented in Chapter 28, **The World's Most Rewarding Hobby**.

The Body Chemistry Support
System provides the necessary
support for the brilliant self-
healing process that our
creator already programmed
into the body, in place of
insulting this wisdom by
trying to "fix" it with
varied treatments.

CHAPTER 23

The Secret To Physical Well-Being Lies In Understanding The Essence Of Life

From a very young age, every child in the U.S. develops a keen awareness that energy is the necessary essence that allows for movement, action and life. We quickly learn that our toys will not work until we put batteries into them. We learn that the radio will not play music until we plug it into an electrical outlet. We also learn a tough lesson associated with our dogs, cats and goldfish. We learn that when the energy of life leaves their bodies, there is no longer movement and we no longer have them as pets.

From observing the mechanical world we can understand the fundamentals of life. Without energy, there is no movement or motion. In fact, "Life" in every form is literally **energy in motion**. No energy, no motion; great energy, great motion; little energy, little motion!

Without an understanding of the essence of electricity, we can still harness it and store it in a battery to bring a wall clock to life. We are able to use large mechanical devices to harness and, as we would identify the process, "generate" electricity for use in our homes.

For decades, mankind has been content to enhance life by harnessing and successfully utilizing this energy without understanding its source. As in every area of life, the deeper our understanding of any subject, the more we are able to benefit from that awareness.

A discussion of the essence of life would not be complete without an acknowledgment of the Source of life, along with a more comprehensive definition and understanding of this essence.

Intuitively, we all know there is one ultimate Source of energy that supports and sustains everything that exists. The problem is that, for thousands of years, the intelligence and awareness of mankind has been evolving from a very simple, primitive and ignorant view of life into an age of nearly unlimited information.

A ten-year-old child can now go to the Internet and gather information on subatomic particles or look at a close-up photograph of Mars. However, let's not forget that only five hundred years ago the top scientists in the world still believed the Earth was flat and that you could sail to the edge and fall off.

Unfortunately, most religious viewpoints regarding the Source of life, or God, have been traditionally handed down without being allowed to evolve at the same rate as man's knowledge and awareness.

The problem caused by this stagnation of awareness is that we all hold a confused image of what the creative source of our lives really is.

Let's imagine for a moment the image of God that has been handed down through time. It has been implied that God is a super-human being who can be everywhere at the same time, who knows everything, and can do anything. As we try to hold this image in our minds, a wiser part of us whispers, "this perspective isn't possible."

With all our science and understanding, the closest we can come to understanding the absolute source of our lives is by observing the essence of the emanations of our Creative Source, which is "energy," the absolute essence of life.

Science has proven to us that even a dense rock is nothing but structured atoms made of energetically structured nuclei with electrons spinning around them. In other words, even rocks are masses of energy; they just vibrate at a lower frequency.

As we consider everything in existence, every single thing—from a rock to a thought—is energy, vibrating at a different frequency.

Therefore, it only makes sense that the Source of All That Is, or God, must be the origin of the highest frequencies of energy. It is like the ultimate tuning fork emanating the highest frequencies of energy. Then, the farther the emanations travel from the Source, the denser the frequencies become.

This is definitely not to imply that God is in one place and a rock is at a point farthest from God. The tapestry of all that exists in our world includes the threads of all frequencies. A great example of this complex grouping of varied frequencies is the high vibration of the sun shining on a lizard's back while he is lying on a rock. This illustrates three very distinct frequencies coexisting in the same place at the same time.

As the emanations of life energy flow through the body of a young human or animal, specific observations become obvious. The greater the volume of this life energy within the body, the more animated the expression. To watch a young kitten playing with a piece of yarn without exhaustion is a great example of the essence of life being expressed. Watching a young goat or colt running and jumping and "feeling his oats" is another example.

The terms that enhance the description of life energy should include vitality, passion, enthusiasm, joy and unconditional love. These energetic expressions naturally occur when a person is "filled with the spirit of life." And when filled with the spirit of life, or the spirit of God, a person is not susceptible to any form of disease. In fact, charge a sick body with enough life force (vitality, passion, enthusiasm and unconditional love) and it becomes impossible for the body to remain ill!

What, then, is the essence of life? It is the emanations of what we have always termed "God."

My favorite old dictionary, one that I've used for years, is a 1943 edition of the *Webster's Collegiate Dictionary*. In this dictionary, the word enthusiasm is defined as: "to be inspired or possessed by the god." In other words, **"the lights are on, and someone is home.**

And when filled with
the spirit of life,
or the spirit of God,
a person is not susceptible
to any form of disease.

CHAPTER 24

Truth

U p to this point, most of the information presented has focused on the explanations of how and why the human body breaks down in all forms of degenerative disease. The remainder of the book will focus on solutions. Don't you agree that it would be a cruel and frustrating trick to describe a problem in such detail without providing solutions? If you are comfortable with what you have read so far, I feel confident you'll love the solutions that follow.

The universally accepted way to guarantee true communication is by establishing clear definitions of the words and terms we use.

Of all the words used in human communication, the word *truth* **is the most central and fundamental starting point for honest communication.**

We have been told that God is the source of all truth. I'm confident we can agree on such a source as being more reliable than a dictionary or any other human standard, but what access do we have to this pure source of defining accuracy? **Every one of us has immediate access to the defining clarity of** *discernment.*

Traditionally, all definitions of the word *discernment* imply that to discern is a process of the mind and intellect, that discernment is a type of keen perception of reasoning and judgment.

I believe that, if we hold to such definitions, we cheat ourselves out of our greatest advantage in life—the way to know the truth that will set us free from the illusions and false perceptions that keep us stuck in what doesn't work for us.

The mind is a very powerful computer. In fact, the mind is the powerful instrument that holds the structure of our entire lives together. However, the mind can only judge, weigh and reason with the information already in its memory banks. **The mind is *not* capable of transferring truth from our Source of truth. If the mind is given an absolute truth and an absolute lie, and supplied with a "logical validation" for each, it is *impossible* for the mind to discern which one is actually true.**

We must be fully aware of this serious shortcoming of the mind. As long as we believe we can mentally reason out our solutions, our lives will remain stuck at their current level. Only through accessing the truth can we free ourselves from the bonds of what we really *don't know*, those areas responsible for the limitations in our lives.

Traditionally, we have been led and directed by individuals in positions of "authority" over us, whether this is in the family, government, school, religion, or the workplace. Those in authority have always assumed the responsibility of knowing what is best for those over whom they have authority. And, if they don't really know at the time what *is* best for the subjects of their authority, the traditional human ego-response has been to authoritatively present their best opinions and claim them as the absolute Truth.

Truth might not always be the most logical solution for everyone involved, but the actual truth is what always works best for the greatest good of all.

There has always been just one way for an individual to know truth—through the process we refer to as intuition. Intuition is pure discernment. Discernment is the one and only way of knowing what really is the truth. Yet, discernment is not a mental process.

At the core of one's soul is his or her heart center. This is our connecting point, our "direct line" to God. Our experience and awareness of this center is usually felt behind the sternum, near the bottom but behind the physical heart. It is quite common to experience awareness in the area between the heart center and the solar plexus. From this area, we get our "hunches," our "gut" feelings, our intuitive awareness, our knowingness of what is true for ourselves. **Again, intuition is pure discernment.**

In speaking to various groups over the years, I have asked this question dozens of times: "How often is our intuition correct?" In every group, I always find a few people who will quickly admit that intuition is always correct. Then there are a few who have never really stopped to think about it. They will nod and say something to the effect of "yeah, intuition is correct most of the time." Within a few seconds of everyone honestly considering this concept, probably for the first time, they unanimously agree that our intuition is always 100% correct. The doubts that get rolled around before being thrown out are discovered to be **the mind's interpretation** of what we intuitively know to be true.

Our intuition is the true power of our discernment. The degree of **trust** we place in our discernment is the degree to which we can know the truth of all things. In this way, we become our own true authorities, through our immediate access to the source of all truth, which is God. Ask and it is given.

Our next concern is exchanging what we really know to be true for the opinions of the "authorities" which we have habitually accepted all our lives. To continually let go of the volumes of opinions we have been handed and replace them with personally discerned truths allows each of us to discover his own best way to enjoy life.

Discernment is the one and only tool that has ever been used to transfer truth from the heart of God to the mind of man, thereby raising human consciousness.

So, always trust what you have discerned to be true!

Of all the words used
in human communication,
the word truth is the most
central and fundamental
starting point for honest
communication.

So, always trust what
you have discerned
to be true!

CHAPTER 25
The Principle of Focused Attention

In Chapter 2, we discussed what a powerful force the Principle of Expectation is in our lives and how the very circumstances of our lives are determined by this principle. **Now we need to discuss a principle that is even greater—The Principle of Focused Attention.**

The Principle of Focused Attention crystallizes our thoughts and opinions into our expectations, and attracts to us the circumstances of our lives. To understand this procedure is like learning firsthand how the genie in the lamp is able to fulfill wishes. This means that very soon **we can become our very own genies!**

Since we cannot separate our emotions from our thoughts, the focus of our attention on any subject is what selects the emotional state we will experience for the length of time we dwell upon the selected subject matter. Just think about that! Whatever subject we choose to hold the focus of our attention upon **automatically** selects for us our emotional states of being. And, as previously stated, our emotional states then regulate the mineral ratios that determine the function of every gland and organ in the body.

I believe it is extraordinarily valuable to thoroughly understand this principle. It is important to take the time to actually list and review each causal step and its associated effect regarding this principle.

Cause #1: We, or someone with whom we are associating, selects a subject. The subject draws our attention, and we naturally focus on the selected subject.

Effect #1: The subject matter automatically activates either a pleasant emotional response within us, such as laughter, excitement, or enjoyment; or an unpleasant emotional response, such as sadness, anger, or sorrow. **Our emotional responses are solicited from our memories of similar experiences and then duplicated** (as detailed in Chapter 4).

Cause #2: Choosing to continue focusing upon a subject that generates unpleasant emotions. (Even if we believe that the subject of our focus isn't of our own choosing, always remember this: **allowing** is a form of choice by default.)

Effect #2a: Holding this focus locks us into a long-term emotional state that begins to distort the minerals within the cells of our bodies. Since our brains cannot tell the difference between an actual experience and a *memory*, when we focus upon an uncomfortable current experience, similar memories are automatically triggered. The brain reviews these similar memories and experiences and categorizes them as *current* experiences. These mentally fabricated experiences are then recorded as new memories, adding to the proof that life is an uncomfortable experience, and confirming a person's already-established expectations of life.

Effect #2b: As the minerals within our cells become distorted, the function of every gland and organ within the body also becomes distorted.

Effect #2c: The second major effect of holding onto an unpleasant focus is the contractive reaction among the tissue cells that closes the pathways through which the essence and substances of life are designed to flow. This directly starves the body of essential nutrients, oxygen, and nerve flow, and, at the same time, poisons the entire body. **The entire foundation for disease is established by this (direct and immediate) effect.**

In the explanation of Effect #2a above, I mentioned how we get locked into a long-term emotional state that begins to distort our mineral levels, leading us into the physical breakdown that culminates in disease. Let's go back to the emotional state immediately prior to the distortion of the mineral levels and discuss what life is like when we get locked into long-term negative emotional states of being. Forget for a moment about the distortion of mineral levels and how the body's health is being distorted. Just think how the quality of our emotional lives is being diminished and the joy of living squeezed right out of us as the more immediate result of our wrong focus. And remember, life isn't a collection of experiences; life is actually an essence, a power! **Life is the energy that animates the human body!**

When the actual life force is removed from our bodies as a direct result of our wrong focus, that is a serious matter. To experience such a loss every once in a while might not be a real threat but, over time, the collective loss of the **energy of life** robs us of the actual essence that makes life worth living. The diminishing of life energy from our bodies is what continually happens when we allow ourselves to engage with our daily stressors; and, without a light at the end of the tunnel or the life within our lives, we lose our purpose for being alive. When this happens to a person, an unconscious decision is made. The unconscious decision is for the soul to leave the body in order to reunite with the joy that has already been forced out of the body. Once this happens, **the greatest treatments on the planet cannot reverse a disease that is unconsciously being used to release the soul.** The only possible way to reverse this mortal decision is to restore hope and joy, which can then change the soul-decision to leave the body.

The Principle of Focused Attention works continually and in accordance with the direction of a person's focus. Because of the power of this principle, when we allow that focus to be drawn into patterns of wrong thought, those patterns can eventually destroy our bodies.

The best way I know to end the automatic focusing in the undesired direction is by healing the traumas responsible for redirecting our focus. The solution will be found in studying and applying the information presented in Chapter 27, **Healing Through The Portals Of Time.** Performing this healing allows us to erase the hurtful expectations that continue to diminish the joy and passion from our lives. Equally important, when this healing is performed, the traumatic memories can no longer demand our attention to be repetitively focused upon painful subjects. When the slate is clean, we become free to create in our lives that which we truly wish to experience.

I submit to you that if we continually apply the Principle of **Focused Attention to the fulfillment of our hearts' desires, the magic that allows each of us to be our very own genie will be revealed!**

When hurtful memories no longer set the stage for our expectations of life, we are free to choose the thoughts that become the seeds of our future experiences. And what are these thoughts of choice? Well, what are the desires of your heart that you wish to experience? What is the blueprint you carry in your heart? What is it that, if you expressed yourself in this manner, would simply make your heart sing? Have you ever allowed yourself the freedom to dare such a dream? Just know that your body and your life will enthusiastically follow the lead of your focus in this direction!

To come to a sure knowledge of what a person really wants in life is one of life's greatest challenges. The reason this is so difficult is because we keep looking in our thoughts for what is so securely hidden in our hearts. To *find* what is in your heart, you must *look* into your heart! When this dream is finally found, it is up to the individual to supply the proper interpretation to express how this dream should look or feel when experienced.

In keeping with the theme of this writing, of course, I would like to point out that your life dream will be at least four times sweeter if you experience that dream with your life energy restored to your body. I maintain that every person who follows The Body Chemistry Support System will be able to restore his life energy—that essence which adds the sparkle back into life.

The Principle of Focused Attention has established the following as an absolute law: **whatever we consistently hold the focus of our attention upon becomes the fabric of our future circumstances.**

As offspring of the creator of our earth, it is the spiritually in-herent power within us as the "focusers" that, as we continually hold our focus on any subject, **the power of our focus expands the value of the subject and endears the subject to us.** This, over time, will automatically weave this subject into our future circumstances.

Another way of looking at this is that, from our heart centers, we have the power of attraction that will draw into our lives any desire we are willing and able to hold a consistent focus upon, **until such time as it is drawn into our lives.** Our challenge is in holding a strong enough focus upon our sincere desire **until** it is drawn into our lives.

Of course, everything needs fuel to power its movement. The powers that draw and attract our dreams and desires are joy, excitement, passion, excited anticipation and enthusiasm. The excitement that naturally occurs with the thought of fulfilling our dreams and desires is enough to eventually draw them into our lives. **However, the more powerfully the thoughts get charged with passion and excitement, the faster they travel!**

This process works every time for every person! It may not work as instantly as a genie, but, really, what are your chances of running into a real genie?

Whatever we consistently hold the focus of our attention upon becomes the fabric of our future circumstances.

CHAPTER 26

The Transitional Perspective Shift From Survival Into Life

Since the beginning of time, mankind has existed in a state of survival. Having no clear memory of life before earthly existence, mankind just naturally expressed itself from this instinctual mode of survival.

The interesting mechanism that evolved for the protection and physical preservation of man was what we now call the "belief system." The ego is the core of this belief system and, no matter what contentions we might have with the ego, we must admit the ego has proven itself quite adept in its capacity for survival.

It's great that survival has successfully kept mankind alive and proliferating, but we are now coming to a time where some serious decisions must be made. We either need to shift from our position of basic survival or be eliminated from the planet. The reason we must make better choices is due to the unwise ways in which we have been consuming our natural resources and polluting the planet. At the same time, we have been rapidly destroying ourselves, as a natural result of the fear-based drive behind human survival.

These statements aren't meant to cause fear or alarm. They are a cautionary wake-up call, reminding us all that, if we continue on our present course of self-destruction, we may soon find ourselves in an environment of our own making that will no longer sustain life on earth.

While avoiding the extinction of all life on earth is a worthy goal, there is a more exciting reason for all humans to engage in this shift, which will allow us to achieve the first goal as well. A level of expression is possible which we have previously only dreamed of. It has been referred to as "heaven on earth." This expression of peace exists as a common blueprint within each of our hearts. The experience of "heaven on earth" will be the natural result for those individuals on earth who make the transitional perspective shift that is presented within this chapter.

Let's review the meaning of **"The Transitional Perspective Shift From Survival Into Life."**

This section began by stating that our entire existence on earth—from the beginning of time to the present—has been, for the most part, an existence of *survival.* We want to review this experience in detail, and then review the necessary shift from survival into an expression of life beyond anything that has ever been previously experienced on earth.

Imagine a group of people who are still alive after their plane crashes in the dense forests of South America. Realizing there is a slim chance of being found and rescued, they decide as a group to start walking to find their way out of the wilderness. As they begin their trek, every member of the group is aware of an unlimited number of ways in which they could die before they find their way to safety.

The circumstances in which this group finds itself are an ideal example of a state of survival. In such a state, the predominant driving force behind their experience is fear! Undoubtedly, any one of us who found himself in such a position would experience the fear of death, the fear of starvation, the fear of being attacked by wild animals, the fear of poisonous snakes and, probably greatest of all, the fear of the unknown. This example underscores the fact that **every form of survival is driven by fear.**

The predominant human expression has always been fear-based, especially where our quest for survival is concerned. Fear causes us to express ourselves as impatient, angry, self-destructive egos. However, there is another expression that has always been available to us—that of loving, benevolent beings. Although we are fully integrated beings, that schism can still cause a profound duality in our behavior.

The truth is that **every one of us** is a loving, benevolent being. The false perception is that we are the impatient, angry, self-destructive fictitious self, called the ego. So, to bring about "The Transitional Perspective Shift From Survival Into Life," we must shift our incorrect perspective of the fictitious characters we have believed ourselves to be. We must remember who we really are as the expression of life in human form.

Beyond everything else, the greatest health secret on earth—for the health of our bodies, the health of our hearts, the health of our emotions, the health of our minds, and the health of our souls—is found when we fully perform this perspective shift.

We always have a choice about the way we express ourselves. We can express ourselves as who we really are, or as we have always believed ourselves to be. Habitually, we generally express ourselves as a suppressed version of the fictitious personality. In order to make the necessary shift, we need to be as clear as possible about where we are shifting *from*, and where we are shifting *to*.

Let's begin with a snapshot of something we intuitively know to be true, and to which pure science can attest as well. At the point of death, life does not just stop, end, or vaporize. The laws of physics maintain that energy cannot be destroyed or brought to a state of nonexistence. You can either convert energy into another form, or you can transfer it to another place, but it is impossible to destroy it.

Most people observing the process of death see the functions of the body slowing down until the heart stops beating, bringing the body to a complete stop, or to the experience we refer to as death. However, many individuals have developed the gift of a finer sight, an extrasensory perception. Such people are able to see what really transpires at the point of death. With their eyes, they may see the body coming to a stop as everyone else does; but often, before the heart stops beating, such gifted individuals are able to "watch" the soul—or the spiritual essence of the individual—leave the body.

This life essence is who we really are. Everything else is just a character role we play, as the fictitious "person." I don't mean to cause confusion by this explanation; my hope is that you will see this as a more functional truth that will provide you a more effective way of shifting your perspective.

Let's review the character traits of the "person" we have believed ourselves to be during this life.

From a true observation of the death experience, we see that the life essence that animates the physical body is what and who we truly are. Therefore, the starting point of defining who we **are not** must begin with the physical body. Below are the components of this fictitious character:

1) Body
2) Brain
3) Personality
4) Ego
5) Belief System

Since who we really are is a spiritual expression of unconditional love, kindness and total acceptance, it should be acknowledged that every expression that is less than these belongs to the fictitious character we have believed ourselves to be.

As Chapter 8 presented, there is only one absolute power that exists—the power of life—which is the essence of our Creative Source, or the expansiveness of all that is. Then there is the "seemingly" opposite, which is contractiveness, or the temporary diminishment of expansiveness.

To apply this principle to the expression of who we really are, as joined with the character we have believed ourselves to be, we claim our relationship to God. This is because, as the essence of life, we are of the same essence. **When we join the human body, we are joining with a substance that has more limited expression.**

The power of who we really are is unconditional love, joy, passion, enthusiasm and all expressions of life, while the driving force of the body, brain, ego, and personality expression is fear. Who we really are has absolutely no reason to experience fear, but the personality we believe ourselves to be knows *only* fear.

It is easy to determine which of our "selves" is being expressed at any given time. We simply need to ask ourselves if our motives are kindness and acceptance, or control and fear of loss.

The ego-self is the author of every fear-based choice of expression. The ego would rather be right than be loved. The ego must always be right, which means it must make others wrong. The ego is always attached to the outcome of every situation. The ego always imposes its own agendas. The ego is always fearful of losing control, because every painful memory is an experience of being out of control. As a reactive, fear-driven machine, the ego is always ready to defend itself. It thrives on drama, and is always ready to judge, condemn, blame, shame, or contend. The fear-based ego does not forgive; it perpetuates agitation, anger, greed, bitterness, discontent, misery, sadness, hopelessness, unhappiness, guilt, self-destruction, **and illness.**

As we observe these traits, remember that **the ego's fear-based survival mechanism makes up the totality of what we call the *belief system*. The belief system is literally like the starter motor on an engine. We need it to start the engine, but when the engine starts, we need to disengage the starter motor because it cannot turn as fast as the engine, and, if it isn't disengaged soon after the engine starts, it can destroy itself and the engine with it.**

Remember that the belief system is comprised of the fear-based survival techniques we have gathered along life's way. That is why we are so willing to aggressively defend our beliefs; we fear that, if flaws were discovered among the opinions that make up our belief system, our very survival would be in jeopardy.

If there were a way to take a person's entire belief system and run it through a shredding machine, what would be left? Our egos would say that we would have nothing left. Yet, if we stop and listen to our hearts, or our intuition, we would hear a resounding, "we would finally have everything!"

It would be great if this shift could just happen in an instant. Maybe an instantaneous shift *is* possible, it's just not very likely. It is for this reason I refer to it as a *transitional* shift. Part of this transition involves an evolutionary shift of maturity that every one of us is working through. This part of the shift requires us to progressively accept responsibility for the authorship of our own lives and stop blaming others for the circumstances of our lives. The degree to which we are able to accept this responsibility is the degree to which we truly set ourselves free to author our lives as we desire.

Let's discuss the strongest reasons for the perpetual "stuckness" that continues to bind us to what doesn't work for us. We have already established how our own traumatic memories, and our inherited traumatic DNA memories, have caused our reduced expectations of life. Joining this awareness with the character traits of the ego will provide a clue to how we get locked into a loop of recreating the circumstances of life that just don't work for us.

As you will recall from the Principle of Focused Attention, **"whatever we consistently hold the focus of our attention upon becomes the fabric of our future circumstances."** A natural and automatic mechanism is continuously at work in our lives that causes us to repeatedly attract the circumstances into our lives that are in harmony with our lowered expectations. Remember, our brains can't tell the difference between an actual experience and a memory! Therefore, every time an old memory gets triggered, even if it is an unconscious DNA memory from one hundred years ago, the brain and emotional system respond as though the experience just occurred.

This brings us to the most important section in this book, and the real work that must be done in order to free us from the grasp of the ego and everything that *doesn't work* in our lives.

If we observe—from the ego's point of view—the way the ego constantly reviews our past traumas, it actually makes sense, especially if we compare this collective memory review to our immune systems.

As survival mechanisms, both the immune system and the ego have direct access to a brilliant memory system. The immune system remembers every attack it has ever engaged in so that it will know exactly how to defend itself the next time it comes under attack by the same unfriendly invaders. In precisely the same way, the ego—which is also a survival mechanism—remembers every traumatic attack so that it will know how to defend itself and thereby survive the next attack.

This is all fantastic for survival but, again, who wants to remain stuck in survival mode when we can learn how to shift into life? No matter how well the ego justifies functioning exactly as it does, it is time for us to disengage from the limiting functions of the ego's survival mechanism.

There is only one way we can effectively disengage from this mechanism—through a diligent application of the true principle of forgiveness.

The dominant attitude in our culture regarding forgiveness has always been that it is our "duty" to forgive our fellow man, and that God's readiness to forgive us requires a corresponding readiness on our part to forgive others. This attitude is generally programmed into every cell of our bodies. The belief is that we have a "duty" or obligation to perform this act and, if we don't, God will simply refuse to forgive us.

I trust that your discernment is as clear as my own on this point. That theory just doesn't add up to the truth of the matter. True forgiveness is an act of the heart, not the ego. The ego is actually *opposed* to the idea of forgiving anyone. The ego would prefer to just get even!

When one considers an act that is being performed out of obligation, and out of fear of disciplinary action, it is useful to remember that the only part of a person that is motivated by fear is the ego. Therefore, we have a real Catch-22 here: an action motivated by fear, performed by a mechanism that has no knowledge of the act and no intention of performing such an action. What I'm saying is that this form of forgiveness will never work.

For decades, the writer and lecturer Harvey Cohen has taught: "If it impacts on you, then it is you." This is a very powerful statement. It distinctly separates us (and our experiences) from the person standing next to us. As we learned from the Principle of Focused Attention, the dominant thoughts we hold on to affect our bodies and lives. When these thoughts activate memories of fear within us, even if the memories are unconscious, the thoughts will join the thousands of similar thoughts as crystallized, contractive **densities** within the body.

Let's consider a few examples of what impacts on a person and how. An obvious example is what we refer to as "being triggered." This happens when a person says or does something that activates a strong emotion within you. If the same words or actions are upsetting to others as well, then it probably isn't a triggering. Regardless of how much it impacts you, if the person next to you is unaffected, this is very likely an example of *you* being triggered. Being triggered is nothing more than the act of a traumatic memory being activated within you. We all carry thousands of these traumatic memories, which are responsible for our reduced expectations of life. They cause the contraction of tissues within the body and lead to a myriad of physical symptoms.

Remember, every reduced expectation, every perceived limitation, every physical distortion, and every symptom, is a manifestation of hundreds of similar thoughts about a false perception we hold somewhere in our collective memories. Every such manifestation can be defined as a crystallized

**mass of thoughts that has been charged with fear! In a nut-
shell, this is the only problem any of us really has.**

The forgoing statements identify the causes of every problem
we have in life. Therefore, all we need do to correct them is find
and apply the right solution. My proposed solution is woven into
The Transitional Perspective Shift From Survival Into Life.
The Perspective Shift takes place as a direct result of the diligent
application of the true principle of forgiveness.

As with every principle, the principle of forgiveness works
every time for every person who applies it in his or her own life.
True forgiveness is an act that must be performed by the heart;
it is definitely not a thought process. Forgiveness, powered by
love, is the only instrument that can reach back through the
portals of time to release and dissolve the false perceptions we
continue to hold on to.

When I say that we continue to hold on to these distorting
false perceptions, let's not forget who that "we" really is. The
person referred to as "me" consists predominantly of the memories and perspectives of eight individuals—the spiritual component that comprises who I really am as an individual, my own
personality, the personalities of my two biological parents, and
the personalities of my four biological grandparents.

Before we get into the solution that forgiveness provides, let's
review the details surrounding the birth of our traumas.

Whether the memory is my own or the cellular memory of a
grandparent as a five-year-old child, the development of the
trauma is quite similar. Every trauma begins with an action
that sparks the discomfort of fear within the individual. When
one person wrongly imposes his will onto another, thereby causing obvious pain or fear, this is one form of trauma. Another
form of trauma occurs when we believe that our basic needs of
life are being threatened. These basic needs include our need to
feel safe from physical harm; the need to feel loved and accepted; the need to have a safe place to live; and the need for
food, shelter and basic care of the body. When any of our basic

needs are threatened, or even appear to be threatened, we experience that as traumatic. Each one of us carries thousands of memories of traumatic experiences, and perceived traumatic experiences. Remember, it doesn't matter whether the trauma was real or only perceived, both are equally contractive and distorting. The only difference is the perceived intensity of each trauma.

Every traumatic experience we hold in memory carries with it the feeling of a perpetual threat. And, since the brain cannot tell the difference between a memory and a current experience, every time a traumatic memory is triggered, the brain and the body chemistry respond as though the trauma has just occurred.

Just for clarity: the ego has immediate access to millions of memories we would consider traumatic. What we refer to as "being triggered" is when the ego compares a current perceived threat to a similar memory from the past, in order to consider all possible solutions. This is a brilliant survival technique! However, the level of awareness involved in this process causes us to experience it all as a very uncomfortable roller coaster ride. This automatic memory review has worked very well up to the present time to keep us alive. The important point to consider now is that mankind has come to a place where it can disengage from the very limiting survival machine and shift into a more unlimited expression of life. I also believe that God, life, and our own souls have been preparing us for this shift.

You could say that **The Transitional Perspective Shift From Survival Into Life** is a magic trick, performed with smoke and mirrors. I don't mean to imply that it entails mystery or that there is a trick to it. What I mean is that there is more to the process than meets the eye, but the shift is simple enough for anyone to accomplish. The smoke represents our false perceptions, or the stories we have attached to each action we have considered to be traumatic. We must be fully aware of the fact that the action we perceived as the cause of our trauma is in the

past and has no effect on us whatsoever—**it** ¡
hold on to that continues to beat us up. The ¡
people and the circumstances in our lives th
and trigger the old stories that must be forg¡
leased.

The shift will take place when we release the traumatic
stories we are holding on to, and re-author our lives in har-
mony with our hearts' desires.

It is now time to discuss the real work that must be done. As
this book has suggested, there is no more rewarding work than
successfully transitioning from survival into life. To begin with,
since illness is a distorted expression of survival and not an expression of life, **once a person has successfully shifted, any**
expression of illness becomes a conscious choice. Not a
very wise choice but, nevertheless, a conscious choice.

We have already established the fact that the one tool we
must use to reach back through the portals of time to release
the traumas is **forgiveness**. The principle of forgiveness is a life-
function, not an activity of survival. Therefore, let's always remember that **love is the power that allows us to use the tool**
of forgiveness to successfully accomplish our desired re-
sults.

Self-evaluation Exercise:

To be fully aware of the release that must be accomplished
through forgiveness, we will begin with a self-evaluation to discover clues that indicate the issues in our lives that require
healing and forgiveness. Of course, we can't blame ourselves for
holding onto the stories that are attached to the experiences we
felt were traumatic to us; but there is an opportunity in the
process to forgive ourselves for holding on.

In your self-evaluation, begin by considering your body as a
communication mechanism. From the top of your head to the
tips of your toes, every sore point, every symptom, every discol-
oration, every blockage, every distortion, every illness, every
sluggish function, and every extra accumulation of substance

that does not belong, indicates a response to the contractive effects of fear held in the body.

It is well worth the time it takes to list every clue to the need for forgiveness. Begin by listing your body indicators. Review the body a few times, and compare every area to when you were twenty years old, then record every problem that has developed since then. Include every scar since you were born, as scars are little records of trauma. Go ahead and list hair loss, loss of hair color, faded eyesight, wrinkled skin, muscles that are in spasm. List everything.

Next, list any emotional abnormalities you notice in yourself. List everything—whether you feel bashful, easily embarrassed, if you believe you speak differently, have a nervous twitch, if you express strong emotions like anger too often, if you have recurring bad dreams or nightmares. Record your pet peeves. Record the things your parents do or have done that irritate you, or things a spouse, child, friend, or co-worker does that irritate you. Record community or world issues that are more irritating to you than to those around you. These are all examples of the truth, "if it impacts on you, then it is you." Specifically consider issues you have had with your parents, brothers or sisters, relatives, spouse, former spouse or lover, friends, co-workers or anyone else to whom you can link current stress. Add these issues to your list.

After your list is complete, review everything and allow yourself to imagine the freedom you will experience with the release and elimination of everything on your list. **To the extent that this is your desire, it can be so.**

I suggest prioritizing your list into groups of ten. Then begin working with the top ten, and later work your way down through the entire list. Work on each group for one month, or until you are satisfied that the whole group has been eliminated. This is the re-creation of who you are. This is a conscious accomplishment in the restoration of who you really want to be.

The writer, philosopher and radio personality Earl Nightingale made a statement that is applicable to this project: "All people are self-made, but only the successful will admit it." Every person who implements this program will be free to successfully re-author his life as he chooses.

Forgiveness is more a state of being than an action. Although forgiveness is an expression of the heart, there is a way of thinking that can actually move us into this heart-based state. This way of thinking includes a review of supportive truths that will prepare us for such important work.

Imagine a second grade teacher standing before her well-behaved class. If you were to ask her about disruptive, naughty children, she might tell you, "there really aren't naughty children, there are only a few sad or hurt children crying out **just a little louder than the others** for love, attention and acceptance."

When a runner is training for a race, he or she will often strap on ankle weights for greater muscle development. There is a psychological advantage to this practice as well. As you can imagine, when the weights are removed, the runner feels as though he or she could almost fly.

I would like to ask you to make a similar preparation for effective forgiveness work. This preparation will make it easy for you to forgive everyone. The only problem with this exercise is that it might take you a while to accept what I'm going to present. Don't let its difficulty bother you. What I'm presenting is an obstacle to every one of us at first. Before you even read the following, ask yourself if you can shift out of your mind and move into your heart so you can do this exercise more successfully.

Without allowing yourself to become emotionally involved, think of a person you believe should *never* be forgiven. Now, for just a moment, release all former beliefs and opinions and move into an intuitive (or non-judgmental) state.

Let's look beyond all our fear-based survival thoughts and find the truth in this matter. Consider this person as he was just prior to joining his human body. At that time, he was—as you and I were before our birth—a loving spiritual being. The body he joined with not only had great potential, but it was programmed with great emotional pain, trauma and strong beliefs.

With this exercise, please understand that I am in no way suggesting that this person's choices and actions should ever be condoned. What I *am* saying is that, if the innocent spiritual essence identified as you or me were placed in that ego/survival mechanism, it is possible that it could have been your soul or my soul that was tormented by the disappointing choices made by the other. This is a true example of the old adage, "there, but for the grace of God, go I." **Each one of us is the essence of life, joy, and love *before* our adventure in the physical world, and we are the essence of life, joy, and love *after* our adventure in the physical world. Only the ego believes differently, and uses that as its excuse for being unwilling to forgive.**

Every human being has this in common: we are always doing the very best we can. Therefore, when we make mistakes it should be remembered that if we knew better, or if we were of a stronger character, we wouldn't have made the mistake. Holding this deeper understanding of who we really are as human beings, let's consider a more extreme example within our personal lives, or those of our parents or grandparents.

Consider a few reasons why a person would want to hurt or take advantage of someone else. In most cases, when a person purposely takes from or hurts another for his personal gain, he justifies his actions by his position in life and the desperation he feels at having to do without what he believes he needs. Just as we feel traumatized when our basic needs are endangered, a perpetrator uses his feelings of desperation at not having what he believes are his basic needs in life as the justification for his actions. Although we might not agree with his justification, from his perspective it makes perfect sense. And, of course, if we were the ones in his shoes, it would make perfect sense to us as well. An attack from such a person is generally the most difficult to forgive, so let's just remember that we really have no obligation to forgive anyone; and it doesn't really do the other person a bit of good to be forgiven. Chances are, the person doesn't really even care whether or not he is forgiven.

The truth of the matter is that I want and need to forgive, for my *own* sake! True forgiveness is a way in which I (that is, all eight of us being expressed through my body) can finally let go of the stories I am holding onto that perpetuate the re-creation of what doesn't work in my life.

Forgiveness is the delete button that erases the stories that establish our expectations of life! **Forgiveness is the actual bridge in our transitional shift from survival into life**. Forgiveness releases us from the dysfunctional controls and the self-destructive patterns of our own egos.

Everything in our lives that doesn't work for us must be forgiven and released. Until we forgive and release, we hold onto and continuously recreate what has hurt us, betrayed us, and what just doesn't work for us. Forgiveness is the only way to dissolve our attachments to that which must be released from our lives.

To first forgive others is the only way I can forgive the person most in need of my forgiveness—myself. Consider once more the eight expressions each of us refers to as "me," and recall the millions of memories we carry from all eight expressions. What could another person do to me that wouldn't activate a mirror of a similar memory within me? **With the collective memory of all eight expressions within me, have I not been guilty of every offense another could impose upon me? And if I, being guilty of a similar offense, cannot forgive my brother or sister before me, how can I ever forgive myself?**

This brings up the deepest, yet most essential, element of the forgiveness principle. **Until we are able to forgive ourselves** for those issues we see mirrored by others in our lives, we will remain un-forgiven. Being un-forgiven generates an unconscious expectation of punishment. With no one else aware of our expectation of punishment, we go on feeling guilty and unpunished. This creates an uncomfortable vacuum in our lives that demands to be balanced. The balance is satisfied by our unconscious punishments through our circumstances and the painful conditions we unconsciously develop within the body!

Stop for a moment and contemplate the true depth of human stuck-ness before proceeding.

Reverting back to the "smoke and mirrors" example, in order to clear the smoke—that is, the stories and dramas attached to the activities in our memories—we must watch our mirrors closely. Our mirrors show up as anyone or anything that triggers any discomfort within us. Being triggered is the signal that something has been impacted within us. **And every impacted issue we hold is in need of forgiveness and healing.** The only way to get to the necessary level of self-forgiveness is by way of the mirrors around us. So, no matter how simple an issue it may be that gets triggered, our highest priority must be to go into our hearts and forgive the mirror in front of us for whatever was said or done. Then, in such a state of forgiveness, the portal is open to reflect our forgiveness back through time to forgive our own offense, so we can finally release it and let it go. Only when this is complete can we stop unconsciously punishing ourselves.

In order to gain the greatest advantages from the principle of forgiveness, we must make forgiveness our favorite tool in the box, and use it on everything. Of course, the starting point should be the top ten items on our priority list. And, rather than treating forgiveness as an action, it is much more powerfully expressed as a "state of being."

Think of forgiveness as the universal problem eraser. When something draws your attention or makes you feel uncomfortable, don't grab onto it or engage with it; simply forgive it and let it pass quietly from your life. This will free you to focus on what *does* work in your life and what truly makes you feel happy.

In the next chapter, **Healing Through The Portals Of Time**, we will cover the practical applications for the principle of forgiveness.

We will shift from survival
into life when we are able
to forgive and release the
traumatic stories we are
holding on to, and re-author
our lives in harmony with
our heart's desires.

CHAPTER 27

Healing Through The
Portals Of Time

I believe there is no more powerful or essential work for each of us to do than the work of healing the pain and traumas from our memories, and from the DNA memories we inherited from our parents. Since these painful memories make up the structure and substance of our negative expectations of life, and since our expectations of life dictate our circumstances, we can never truly be free to live a deeply satisfying life until the negative power of these traumatic memories has been diffused through our forgiving, healing, and releasing them.

A deeper understanding of the Principle of Triggering is the doorway leading to successful healing.

When we are triggered, we experience an automatic, knee-jerk reaction that strongly disrupts our present peace and comfort. Sometimes this reaction causes us to feel inhibited and incapable of expressing how we feel. Other times it causes us to feel overpowering fear, anger, or sadness.

The Principle of Triggering is the link between our here and now, and that which waits within to be healed.

That is what makes this work the most challenging for us to master—we must perform our greatest healing in the face of being triggered.

Imagine a pistol. Every pistol has a trigger. Have you ever heard of anyone being hurt by a trigger? Of course not, a trigger is a release mechanism allowing the hammer to activate the bullet.

In considering the Principle of Triggering for healing, it is important to understand that, when we get triggered, the "bullet" that seems to be causing the real problem is not a present issue at all, but an **activated memory from the past.**

Because of the vast amount of neural firing that takes place within the brain, we commonly, but wrongly, consider the brain to be the center of our mental activity. In reality, when we get triggered, there is a strong sensation in the solar plexus area. This area is actually a very powerful focal point of **mental** activity. This point is the area of our "gut" feelings, where we get those hunches that are always so accurate. The strong sensation is mainly due to the powerful bond that exists between thoughts and emotions and the way they are energetically focused within the solar plexus area of the body. This area is our alarm center, the junction point where the self-preservation intelligence for the body evaluates anything that is perceived as a possible threat. Once this split-second evaluation has been performed, a chemistry alarm is instantly sounded throughout the body and the body responds according to the level of the perceived threat.

Interestingly enough, like the brain, this survival alarm system isn't capable of determining the difference between an actual experience and a memory. Therefore, even if a DNA memory is triggered, not only would the brain treat this memory as a current event, but the alarm would sound to the level the brain perceived the memory as a threat. **The memory-activated chemistry duplicating system** detailed in Chapter 4 is what guarantees the body's ability to respond to the impending threat exactly the way it always has and, thereby, assure our survival yet another day.

It should now be very clear why our knee-jerk reaction to being triggered feels like such a deep, defensive, primitive response. The attacks on our ancestors by wild animals and barbaric people originally programmed this survival alarm system. This is the reason we sometimes feel as though our very survival is being threatened when we get triggered.

As mentioned before: **The Principle of Triggering is the link between our here and now, and that which waits within to be healed.**

With the benefit of this clarity, a person's mindset must shift from a defensive survival stance to a kind and loving mode of forgiveness. It's our only way to reach those issues in need of healing. Our defensive stance keeps us locked in hell, while forgiveness frees us to make the transition into a heavenly state of joy.

There is so little time, and so much baggage to release. Every discomfort should be celebrated as an opportunity to forgive, release and let go. There is only one way to get from where we don't want to be to where we want to be—that is to forgive, release, and let go; forgive, release, and let go; forgive, release, and let go!

Two techniques can be employed **to heal the causes of every discomfort in our bodies and in our lives.** The first is the Principle of Triggering, which can be used to heal through the portals of time. The second is a continual process of forgiveness.

The most difficult part of the first technique is that the healing must be performed the moment someone or something has triggered you. This is exactly the time most of us would prefer to run away, defend ourselves, or maybe just slip out and have a chocolate bar. Yet, this is the only time the work can be done effectively.

It is best if our minds are prepared, **before we get triggered,** for how we will respond when we are triggered. Being triggered often catches us off guard. We are usually deep into a whole new drama by the time we wake up and realize that we chose a less mature way of dealing with being triggered...again. **Our state of mind must always be: "nothing matters more than healing my traumas and, no matter what I think is happening, I must give everyone the benefit of the doubt, because I'm using every experience as an opportunity to heal!"**

First Technique Of Healing Through The Portals Of Time:
When you view every trigger as a healing opportunity, you will

maximize your success by doing the following. Every time someone or something makes you feel uncomfortable, immediately direct your attention toward your solar plexus and, with all the love and compassion you can generate, imagine yourself holding a younger version of yourself who feels hurt, sad and lonely. As you hold this younger person, reassure him or her by repeating: **"you are not alone, I am here with you. What you are going through will be just fine because it isn't your fault. Don't worry about what is happening because it's going to be okay."**

Just keep repeating those statements with as much love and compassion as you can for about fifteen seconds, **and the healing is done!** This is the first and most important technique for Healing Through The Portals Of Time. Repeat it every time you get triggered, feel any emotional discomforts, a low level of energy, or anything less than how you want to feel. After a week or two of this form of healing, you will discover you are no longer as reactive to people or events; you are healing some major issues.

Watch out for your mind, though, as it tends to be impatient with this process that undermines its control! In fact, as you become emotionally healthier, the ego will begin to panic and will often justify the things people do, and tell you that you really aren't triggered and to not worry about it. **Don't listen; keep healing!**

Second Technique Of Healing Through The Portals Of Time:

The second technique is much easier, because you can do it whenever you wish. Remember, each technique is for a specific need; they should not be used interchangeably. The first technique is the only one to use when you get triggered, and it must be used **at that moment.** The second technique should be done at least twice daily. This technique is best done in conjunction with the best exercise in the world—bouncing on a mini trampoline. By combining these two techniques, your results will be **predictably assured**.

If you haven't yet made your priority list of physical and emotional discomforts, refer back to Chapter 26. Take a regular size piece of paper (8 ½" x 11") and write your top ten discomforts in large print. Mount your list onto a piece of cardboard or attach it to the wall in front of your trampoline.

Before engaging in this powerful releasing and healing procedure, take time to memorize the following paragraph. It must be memorized well enough for you to repeat it without having to think about it. This will allow your entire focus to be directed to the issues being forgiven and released.

First option: "Whatever or whomever activated the fear I have held within my [name the area of your body], I now forgive, release and let go. . . allowing for the expansiveness of life to flow freely throughout my entire body."

Second option: "Whatever or whomever activated the fear I have held onto, I now forgive, release and let go. . . allowing for the expansiveness of life to flow freely throughout my entire life."

The first option is for releasing physical densities from your body. The second option is for releasing fear-based beliefs from your life.

Let's suppose you are ready to release tension from your neck muscles. Why are these muscles so tight? This is the place a person most commonly holds his self-imposed burdens of life. And, of course, this is a result of holding onto at least one fear-based false belief regarding what one must accomplish in life in order to be seen as acceptable.

Let's say this is the first entry on your list of ten top priorities to be released from your body and life. If you can, as you are comfortably jumping on a mini trampoline, spread your fingers and place your fingertips over the area of tension, while reviewing the thought. Review the thought while **feeling** as deeply as possible the ideas you are expressing. Your first density to be released is a physical contractiveness; use the words, "held within the muscles of my neck" as the area of your body. Finish by allowing the expansiveness of life to flow freely "throughout my entire body." If you are releasing an emotional issue, such as an anger response you copied from your father, simply use the second option written above.

Here's the good news: it is much easier to actually *do* this process than it is to read the instructions for it!

If you jump on your trampoline for fifteen minutes twice every day, this will become a powerful prayer time or meditation period. During this time, you can accomplish work that is more liberating than you ever imagined. It works like no other tool available for this purpose. Just don't expect it to dissolve forty years of self-destruction on the first day.

As you move down your list of the top ten densities that need to be removed from your body and your life, you will have time to review each one four or five times. As you do this work, keep intensifying your feelings. The more emotion you put into it, the faster you will produce results.

Let's review a few more details about the way our thoughts crystallize into our circumstances and cause the distortions within our bodies. That way, as we are healing what we unintentionally created in the past, **the way we are dismantling the destructive forms from our bodies and our lives will be clarified.**

Have you ever heard the statement, "thoughts are things"; or "thoughts are creative"?

Everything, from a thought to a piece of steel, is comprised of energy. Everything is made up of organized and structured particles of energy that manifest at different frequencies.

A conscious thought is a creative, organizing, molding mechanism. Mankind has been endowed with the privilege of possessing the inherent gift of creative thought. This means that every thought of man is inherently creative.

Thoughts can be likened to fine particles of water. There is always water in the air we breathe, but only when enough water particles group together under the correct environmental conditions can we see the water as clouds, rain or snow.

Every thought we think is a structured mass of energy. On its own, the thought lacks the power and the volume to manifest in an observable form. A second, similar thought also lacks power and volume but, because of the principle of universal attraction, the second thought attaches to the first, forming the beginning of a thought cluster. From the beginning of a thought cluster, time and focus determine when this thought cluster will possess the power and the volume to manifest itself as a part of our lives.

Every thought is creative, and every creation has purpose and is good. Yet, there comes a time when our lives can serve a greater purpose by moving beyond creations that no longer serve us. Some of our unintentional creations from the past are examples of this.

Remember, life serves us and enhances our experiences, while every diminishment of life inhibits us and limits our experiences. In the past, we (by "we," I mean all eight expressions of who we are) have unintentionally created many obstacles for ourselves. These have served us well by providing the necessary resistance against which we have struggled to become strong. This has been useful and beneficial for the thousands of years during which the general belief was that "what doesn't kill you makes you stronger" (*Nietzsche*). We have begun to realize that what doesn't kill you may make you stronger for a time, but it will eventually break you down and kill you. Of course, I am referring again to our stressors.

Life is really much simpler than we give it credit for being. There are, basically, those things that enhance our lives and those things that detract from our lives.

Logic would suggest that man would simply select what enhances his life and leave alone what detracts from life. Due to the automatic duplicating effects of the ego's survival system, we now understand that man has been guilty of unintentionally re-creating unwanted self-destructive expectations for thousands of years. Since this was an automatic response, and specific principles of the universe supported its continuation, mankind remained stuck in this never-ending cycle.

If you review your self-evaluation list from Chapter 26, you will see that most of your unintentional creations **detract** from your life. These thought clusters in your life must be dismantled.

Let's keep this dismantling process very simple. Every thought, as it is birthed, is charged with either a form of love or life—which is expansive—or fear, which is contractive. Every thought cluster that detracts from your life is charged with the emotion of fear. Every thought cluster that enhances your life is charged with some aspect of love.

Every distortion on your self-evaluation list is an obvious example of a thought cluster structured from fear-charged thoughts. These are all manifestations of contractiveness that diminish and/or detract from your life.

A spasm in a muscle is a manifestation of a thought cluster charged with fear. Every stressful issue in life is a manifestation of a thought cluster charged with fear. Every form of illness is a manifestation of a thought cluster charged with fear. Anything and everything that takes away from the fullness of your life is a manifestation of a thought cluster charged with fear.

Have you ever watched a demolition crew at work? Luckily, to demolish a structure usually only takes about a tenth of the time as the original construction.

Think about what happens to any mass when the expansiveness of life is drawn from it. The mass becomes denser. When the energy is withdrawn from an atmosphere, a cloud forms. The lower the energy, the more dense the substance.

Compare this principle to the human body by considering the energy difference between a live body and a dead body.

In the process of forgiveness, every time you review the thought, "whatever or whomever activated the fear I have held within my body and life, I now forgive, release and let go...allowing for the expansiveness of life to flow freely throughout my entire body and life," you weaken the cluster toward which you are directing the forgiveness. Everything that takes away your joy for living—every distortion, every density, and every stressor—is a negative cluster that must be forgiven and released.

All expressions of life and love are like solvents that dissolve negative clusters. Every negative cluster can be dissolved. If you have a stubborn, well-established cluster, just charge it with more passion as you continue forgiving and releasing it.

How long do you think we should continue with our twice-daily practice of dismantling negative clusters? **I propose that we continue right up to the time we can honestly and passionately claim we are living our lives according to our grandest dreams.**

The Principle of Triggering
is the link between our
here and now, and that
which waits within
to be healed.

CHAPTER 28

The World's Most Rewarding Hobby

An important part of living a balanced life is the willingness to enjoy at least one hobby that allows you to express your talents and abilities in a non-occupational way. A hobby can be anything one chooses, such as joining others in playing a favorite sport or maybe coaching a sport. A hobby can be playing with big kids' toys, such as all-terrain vehicles. Many creative hobbies enhance not only the life of the hobbyist, but also the lives of those who enjoy his creations.

The restoration of a classic automobile is a hobby that I think best exemplifies the principles I would like to emphasize.

The beauty of a fully restored classic car is something most people can appreciate. Yet, most of us aren't sufficiently motivated to take on the arduous task of converting a pile of scrap metal found in a wrecking yard into a showcase beauty. However, all the beautifully restored cars found in this country attest to the fact that thousands of highly motivated individuals are willing to expend the necessary efforts to convert auto salvage into a work of art.

Let's review an example of one of the easiest restoration projects—a 35-year-old car that has all its original parts.

Remember, for this to be a fully satisfying hobby for our auto enthusiast, we have to observe a few "hobby rules." The journey, no matter how difficult, must provide the individual with an enjoyable challenge and exercise his or her talents and abilities. The hobby cannot be just the endurance of hard labor in exchange for the resulting accomplishment. A hobby isn't a replacement for other responsibilities or obligations or an escape from life. A hobby is a balanced outlet that enhances an individual's life.

A hobby usually requires an investment of at least a few

hours every week, and most creative hobbies require an additional financial investment for the purchase of new parts and supplies.

To transform a 35-year-old car into a showcase beauty might take from one to three years, depending upon the hobbyist's level of commitment.

The car must first be disassembled. The body must be taken off the frame. The engine, transmission and the drive assembly must all be removed. The body must be sandblasted and any rusted metal either replaced or repaired. The frame must be sandblasted and repaired. The engine, transmission and drive assembly must all be completely rebuilt. When everything is cleaned and repaired, every piece must be repainted and re-assembled.

During this whole process, the hobbyist can perform the majority of the labor. This will allow the project to be accomplished for a reasonable amount of money. Obviously, if the hobbyist saw himself as being the overseer of the project, and hired all the work to be done by others, it would be a much more expensive project.

A few areas may exist in which the hobbyist lacks the necessary knowledge or skills to finish the project. Sometimes the answer can be found in taking a few classes. In other cases, it is best to seek the help of a specialist.

Woven into the explanation for rebuilding a classic car are most of the principles for engaging in the World's Most Rewarding Hobby.

There are very few assets a person could claim as more valuable than the efficient functioning of his or her own body. **What we refer to as the health of our bodies is what determines the quality and enjoyment of every other experience in our lives.** When a person is in constant pain or fatigue or feeling ill, this darkens every experience.

Because of the renewed joy of life and the restored purpose in the lives of those who have fully restored their true health, I'm convinced there isn't a more rewarding hobby in

the world than the hobby of fully restoring health to the body.

Most of us are guilty of taking much better care of our cars than our bodies. We know that if we don't keep the car serviced properly, it will break down. We also know that if we put diesel fuel in the gas tank, the car won't run. Because we don't want to be inconvenienced with breakdowns, we keep our cars serviced and running well. Unfortunately, we don't see our bodies in the same light. As adults, we have been much more aware of our self-abuses than we care to admit. **We just need to realize that if we are willing to roll our sleeves up and do the work, most of the damage can be reversed.**

This entire book has been dedicated to clarifying the reasons why the human body breaks down in all forms of disease and to offering support in reversing the damage.

Four major projects must be successfully completed before true health can be restored to the body, and they have been presented quite clearly throughout this book. The four projects are:

- Removing a lifetime accumulation of toxic waste from all pathways of the body.
- Reversing the accumulated damage throughout the body.
- Healing the traumas found at the core of all disease, and responsible for all reduced expectations.
- Restoring the lost essence of life back into the body.

The only way all this work can be accomplished in a reasonable amount of time is as a habit, a daily challenge to which an individual is willing to dedicate the time and effort. It must be considered part of everyday life for at least three years.

If a person is willing to make an honest commitment to himself, and consistently follows the outlined program, all four projects listed above can be accomplished in a three-year period.

Outline For The 36-Month Life Restoration Program:

1) The entire program begins with a two-week prep kit. This gets the body accustomed to being supported in a complete enough way for it to begin normalizing its own functions.

2) The next phase is the 30-Day Life Restoration Challenge. This is the most powerful total-body detoxification program there is. This 30-day period will not only detoxify the body in the most efficient manner, it will align an individual with his or her own intuition more effectively than any other technique.

3) For the next five months, the complete Body Chemistry Support System must be followed to keep up the momentum began by the 30-Day Challenge. After the five-month period is over, the 30-Day Challenge is repeated. During the 36 months, the Body Chemistry Support System must be followed continuously in between the twice-yearly 30-Day Challenges.

4) Every day, as a major focus and as part of an exercise program, the two exercises in the *Healing Through The Portals Of Time* program must be done.

This is the only complete program available for accomplishing everything necessary to turn a person's life around. I apologize if it seems to be a lot to do. Just trust that we can and will mentor you to your successful completion.

Most importantly, I guarantee you will find it to be, without exception, *The World's Most Rewarding Hobby!*

What we refer to as the
health of our bodies is
what determines the
quality and enjoyment
of every other experience
in our lives.

CHAPTER 29

Human Biorestorology

As you now clearly understand, when a person has removed the lifetime accumulation of toxic debris from the body, reopened the five pathways where life is meant to flow, and healed the major traumas responsible for destructive contractiveness, it now becomes possible to restore the essence of life to the human body.

When the essence of life is restored to the body, all contractiveness is relaxed and released, allowing the old accumulated damages to finally be healed, and an ultimate level of health to be enjoyed. This is a great and rewarding accomplishment that will open the door to a whole new, and abundant, expression of life.

Since there are areas of this work we can't always do for ourselves, remember that there are professionals who have been trained to assist us in these endeavors. This is the true purpose for the work of chiropractors, acupuncturists, colon hygienists, physical therapists, massage therapists, and the many other professionals whose work it is to assist in the reopening of the pathways of life.

In the near future, as people grow more intolerant of the huge profits that are being generated from human suffering, all forms of treatment involving drugs will either be discontinued or turned toward enhancing the well being of the body, rather than just bringing temporary relief to symptoms. With such a focal shift, treatment can then join the newest branch of the healing arts, referred to as Human Biorestorology. **The term Human Biorestorology simply means "The Science Of Restoring The Essence Of Life To The Human Body."**

The purpose and function of Human Biorestorology is to apply the principles that determine the well being of the

human body so fully and consistently that the body is capable of restoring the essence of life and healing itself completely.

This may seem like a radical thought when viewed from a paradigm that is still hoping to discover "cures" for what is falsely believed to be external forces attacking the human body and causing the various degenerative diseases.

Yet, from the viewpoint of Human Biorestorology, when the body is fully detoxified and all nutrients are made available, the five pathways of life are reopened, and the traumas have been healed, then the wisdom of the body is completely free to accomplish the work it previously struggled in vain to accomplish.

The starting point and the core of Human Biorestorology is The Body Chemistry Support System. From the starting point of Body Chemistry Support, a person would look to the ways that have been developed and the professionals who have been trained to assist in the reopening of the five pathways of life. This includes the professionals mentioned in the third paragraph above as well as many others in the healing arts whose training allows them to assist an individual in the work of reopening all five pathways so that life can fully flow throughout the body once again. And last, but definitely not least, is the important work of healing the traumas responsible for almost all of the stress we experience in life.

If it is too difficult in the beginning to do "Healing Through The Portals Of Time," there are many caring counselors whose expertise can make the work of healing traumas much easier to accomplish.

Then, as you engage in the work of forgiving, releasing and Healing Through The Portals Of Time, all levels of cause for all degenerative disease will be eliminated and you will be free to create whatever level of health and happiness you desire.

The purpose and function of Human Biorestorology is to apply the principles that determine the well being of the human body so fully and consistently that the body is capable of restoring the essence of life and healing itself completely.

CHAPTER 30

Living With Passion—Our Natural State Of Being

As I reflect back on the day I first met Steve, I can't help but smile. He looked like an excited little boy on his way to Disneyland. He was dressed like the Marlboro man, wearing jeans and cowboy boots, with his hands in the pockets of his bulky, wool-lined leather coat. He walked into his real estate office glowing like the captain of the high school football team who had just won the big game. The confident glow in his eyes and the permanent smile on his face was like a warm fire on a chilly December morning.

It isn't often, but occasionally a person comes along who is actually living his life with passion. You can see it in his face and hear it in his voice. In fact, you can actually feel it radiating from his whole being. To be in the presence of such a person makes life feel safe and wonderful. While in his presence, the harshness of life just seems to fade away, leaving a feeling that only good things can happen.

What is so different about Steve? What power does he possess that seems to be lacking in most of mankind? Is it possible that life has given that magical something to a very select few, allowing them to live charmed lives, while everyone else struggles in misery?

Not every person on earth has inherited buckets of trauma and the expectation that life is out to destroy him—just most. That's why I believe this book is a helpful tool. There just aren't many individuals like Steve in the world. Therefore, the rest of us, who do have traumas to heal, just have some work to do on the way to creating a similarly charmed life.

No matter how beautiful the paint color you buy, until it gets applied to the wall its true value remains locked away as potential.

A wonderful fact of life that can be a source of hope and motivation for all of us is that, if one person is able to accomplish a particular feat, anyone else who has the desire may follow the exact steps and duplicate that accomplishment. It is my intent to demonstrate that each of us has everything necessary to create a deeply satisfying and enjoyable "charmed life."

About a week after I met Steve, he invited my wife and me to dinner, along with the couple that first introduced us to Steve.

Steve lived in a small, but very comfortable, two-bedroom home with his wife and young daughter. In their living room was a wood stove they used to heat their home. The stove had two levels of flat surfaces on which Steve's wife, Pam, was excitedly demonstrating her recently acquired wood stove cooking skills. The look on her face was the same as a little girl who had just put out her new tea set and invited her friends over for tea.

While the women sat around the stove visiting, Steve invited Dick and me down to his basement to show us his new hobby. A few weeks earlier, Dick took Steve target practicing with pistols and, at the time, mentioned the store where Steve could buy the tools and supplies for reloading his own bullets. Just like a kid showing his buddies what he got for Christmas, Steve showed Dick and me the bullets he had reloaded.

The spirit that permeated Steve's home that night was uniquely special. It was as though Steve and Pam had captured the most vital elements of childhood, and filled their lives and home with its gentle essence. To understand the treasure Steve and his family shared and enjoyed, and especially to discover a way of enticing this essence into one's personal life, would be to gratify the sweetest dream in the heart of every person.

In looking back on childhood, most of us have memories that make us wish we could go back and repeat those experiences. Yet, at the same time, we have to admit that a lot of our childhood experiences weren't so enjoyable. I believe each of us has a feeling, like a blueprint we carry in our hearts, of our *ideal* childhood expression. This is a vision of the childlike traits that exemplify the innocence of childhood. If these traits were listed and reviewed, and we could find a way to express them through our personal lives, I believe we would have the secret for duplicating the special essence that permeated Steve's home and family.

As I reflect on my observations of Steve's life, I see a man who very wisely held to the qualities of an ideal childhood, and wove those qualities into his adult life. Let's consider what some of those qualities are, with the intention of reproducing them in our own lives.

I think we would all agree that the greatest difference between children and adults is found in their energy levels. Next would be the hopeful, trusting, innocent way a child perceives all of life.

A child, just like a kitten or any other young animal, looks for every possible opportunity to play. If children don't have something to laugh about, they will create a reason to laugh. Through the eyes of a child, life is an unlimited adventure with unlimited opportunities for discovery. A child believes there is no end to the supply of life's energy. A child doesn't know even a fraction of what an adult knows about how dangerous life can be. Children are so focused on living that they don't see all the inhibiting obstacles so closely viewed by most adults. By healing the pain from our memories, we can start forgetting how scary and dangerous life appears. Then we can remember that life really is an exciting adventure.

When and how did we lose our childlike qualities? At what point did we agree that life was so harsh and serious that we stopped really living? It was at that exact moment that we chose to redirect our focus. By default, adults develop a focus on what needs to be done, what must be fixed, how much money is needed to keep up, how to protect those we love from being hurt or killed, and on and on.

There are two solutions to this important problem. First, clean the slate by healing the traumas; and, second, literally take out a notebook and pen (or computer) and start writing your clearest interpretation for the blueprint of your dream-life—from your heart.

What a concept! Here I am the sole author of my immediate life, with the blueprint of my ideal life hidden within my heart, with my trauma-induced expectations of life dictating the limitations of my life, and I wonder why I feel that my life remains unfulfilled.

Although all of us carry a blueprint in our hearts of our dream-lives, as we heal and improve our expectations of life, our interpretations of these dream-lives will become clearer to us. Therefore, we need to review our descriptions often and make the necessary adjustments to the details.

When we have healed the reasons for feeling unworthy from the past, and have confidently authored our dream-lives, we become free to advance our way to the meeting point of our dream-lives. And, along the way, we will find that it gets easier and easier to restore the innocent child-like qualities we lost along life's way. As Albert Einstein said in describing this process: **"the pursuit of truth and beauty is a sphere of activity in which we are permitted to remain children all our lives."**

"The pursuit of truth and beauty is a sphere of activity in which we are permitted to remain children all our lives."

Albert Einstein